Teacher's Manual with Lesson Plans and Answers

Contemporary Chemistry
THE PHYSICAL SETTING

Paul S. Cohen
Former Assistant Principal-Supervision-Science
Franklin Delano Roosevelt High School
Brooklyn, New York

D1192542

AMSCO

Amsco School Publications, Inc.
315 Hudson Street, New York, N.Y. 10013

When ordering this book, please specify: **R 769** T
CONTEMPORARY CHEMISTRY: THE PHYSICAL SETTING
TEACHER'S MANUAL WITH LESSON PLANS AND ANSWERS

ISBN: 0-87720-111-0

Copyright © 2004 by Amsco School Publications, Inc.
No part of this book may be reproduced in any form without
written permission from the publisher.

Printed in the United States of America

1 2 3 4 5 6 7 8 9 10   09 08 07 06 05 04

To the Teacher

This Teacher's Manual is designed to provide assistance to new as well as experienced teachers. The author, an experienced chemistry teacher, shares the insights he has gained during his more than 25-year career.

The book has two parts: The Lesson Plans and the Answer Key. At the beginning of the lesson plan for each chapter, there is a brief introduction to the topics covered. A grid that lists possible lesson titles, reading assignments, and homework assignments follows the introduction.

Unless otherwise noted, each lesson is intended for a single, 40- to 45-minute period. The lesson plans follow the grid. Each plan incorporates several related topics from the grid and covers several days of work. Suggested laboratory activities follow the lesson plans.

The Answer Key provides answers (and, where appropriate, solutions) to all Practice, Chapter Review, Constructed Response, and Chemistry Challenge questions, and the questions in Appendix 1.

Contents

1 *Matter and Energy*

INTRODUCTION

The first chapter includes gas laws, phase change, and heat calculations. Some teachers may prefer to move on to Chapter 2, "Atomic Structure," before dealing with phases and gas laws; it is recommend that they make the jump before "Energy and Changes of State" on page 16. Historically speaking, however, the gas laws predate the discovery of the atom, and can easily be presented first, as in this text.

Day	Lesson for the Day	Text pages	Homework
1	How do we study matter?	1 to 5	
2	Physical and chemical properties	5 to 6	Pg. 7, Practice 1.1, 1.2
3	Physical and chemical change	6 to 9	Pg. 7, Practice 1.3
4	Elements, compounds, and mixtures	10 to 13	Pg. 13, Practice 1.4–1.7
5	Potential and kinetic energy	14 to 16	Pg. 57, Chapter Review 1
6	Energy and phase change	16 to 18	Pg. 18, Practice 1.8–1.11
7	Measurement of heat	18 to 23	Pg. 22, Practice 1.12–1.17
8	Drill, matter and energy (This is one of our longer chapters. Teachers may find it prudent to pause here for review, and perhaps for an examination.)	57 to 62	Pgs. 57–62, Chapter Review 8, 10, 21, 26, 28, 36, 37; Pg. 62, Constructed Response 3
9	Properties of gases	23 to 30	Pg. 30, Practice 1.20–1.23
10	Boyle's Law	31 to 33	Pg. 33, Practice 1.24–1.26
11	Charles' Law	33 to 35	Pgs. 35–36, Practice 1.27–1.29
12	Combined Gas Law (Include Gay-Lussac's Law in this lesson.)	36 to 38	Pg. 38, Practice 1.31, 1.32
13	Ideal gas law* and Avogadro's Hypothesis	38 to 40	Pg. 39, Practice 1.33, 1.34
14	Other gas laws—Dalton's Law, Graham's Law, deviations from ideality	40 to 44	Pg. 43, Practice 1.35, 1.36
15–16	Liquids—Vapor pressure (2 days)	44 to 49	Pgs. 49–50, Practice 1.37–1.42
17	Solids	50 to 53	Pgs. 52–53, Practice 1.43–1.46
18	The phase diagram**	53 to 55	

* Ideal gas law and calculations using R are omitted from many basic chemistry courses.
** Phase diagrams are often omitted from basic chemistry courses, but are included on national examinations, such as the SAT II.

TOPIC I *The Nature of Matter (4 days)*

Goal: How do chemists classify and study matter?

Instructional Objectives

Students will be able to:
1. Define matter, energy, element, compound, mixture, and substance.
2. Use physical and chemical properties to describe matter, and distinguish between the two.
3. Distinguish between physical and chemical change.
4. Identify various chemicals as element, mixture, or compound.

Motivation for the Topic

Pour sodium chromate crystals onto a watch glass. Ask students to identify the substance, and ask them how they know. (They will usually guess that it is sulfur.)

Pour some sulfur onto a second watch glass. Which is the sulfur? Demonstrate that only one of the solids is soluble in water. Solubility is one of the properties used to study matter.

Development of the Topic

Have students use such properties as odor and density to distinguish between substances, such as water and alcohol, lead and aluminum. List, as typical physical properties, state, color, odor, density, and solubility. Bright students may also suggest melting point and/or boiling point; these should certainly be accepted, and can be demonstrated.

Next, pour some water into one evaporating dish, and ethanol into another. What is another way we could determine which is the alcohol? Show that alcohol is combustible while water is not. How is this property, combustibility, different from the others we listed? Distinguish a chemical property from a physical property. Take out two test tubes, previously prepared, one with water, the other with dilute HCl. Tell the students that one of these is water, and drop a piece of Mg ribbon into both. Did we use a chemical property or a physical property to distinguish the water from the acid? Explain.

In discussing physical and chemical change, introduce the concept of endothermic and exothermic change. Students always have difficulty with the idea that freezing is exothermic, and that boiling is endothermic. Emphasize that bond breaking is always endothermic, while bond formation is always exothermic. Endothermic physical changes that can be demonstrated include the dissolving of ammonium nitrate in water. The rapid crystallization that occurs when an extra crystal is added to supersaturated sodium thiosulfate is exothermic. There is, of course an enormous number of possible exothermic chemical changes you might demonstrate. Try something pretty, like the addition of concentrated NH_3, and then concentrated HCl, to a solution of copper sulfate. For an endothermic chemical change, stir a mixture of barium hydroxide and ammonium thiocyanate in a small beaker. If you place the beaker on a wet wooden block, the mixture gets cold enough to freeze to the block. The odor of ammonia, a new substance formed in the reaction, is evidence that this is a chemical change.

To motivate a discussion of elements, mixtures, and compounds, you can show the class copper strips, a new penny that has been cut in half (revealing the zinc interior), and a crystal of copper sulfate. Point out that all these samples contain copper—elicit the differences. This is a good time to distribute periodic tables, and to identify some of the types of elements, such as metals and nonmetals. Distinguish homogeneous mixtures, such as solutions, from heterogeneous mixtures. Explain why mixtures are not true substances, while elements and compounds are. Show a sample of brass, and encourage students to classify it as element, mixture, or compound— what questions would one need to ask?

TOPIC II *Energy in Chemical and Physical Changes (3–4 days)*

Goal: How is energy involved in chemical and physical change?

Instructional Objectives

Students will be able to:
1. Distinguish between exothermic and endothermic change in terms of potential and kinetic energy.
2. State the law of conservation of energy.
3. Draw and interpret heating and cooling curves of pure substances.
4. Perform calculations based on the equation

   heat = mass × change in temperature × specific heat

Motivation for the Topic

Announce that you are about to perform a feat of incredible courage. You will heat an object in the hottest part of a flame for thirty seconds. You will then hold the object firmly in your hand for a full minute. Permit your students to suggest how you will accomplish this. Then take out a large piece of ice, and hold it in the flame. Why is it not getting hot?

Development of the Topic

Draw a heating curve for water, from −20°C to 120°C. Elicit the key breaks in the curve from your students. What is happening during the parts of the curve where the temperature is constant? Identify the five segments of the curve. Identify the heat absorbed in melting the ice as the heat of fusion, and the heat absorbed in boiling the water as the heat of vaporization. You may wish to provide the actual values at this point.

Emphasize that melting and boiling are both endothermic changes. What is happening in terms of energy? Kinetic energy, from the heat source, is being converted to potential energy, as bonds are broken. Provide a heating curve of a second substance, and have students find the melting, boiling, and freezing points. Repeat with a cooling curve.

If you wish to provide opportunities for further graphical analysis, provide a heating curve that lists the quantity of substance and rate of heating in joules/minute. Have students calculate the heat of fusion of the substance, in joules/gram, based on the time required for the substance to melt.

The next day, refer back to the heating curve, and ask students to distinguish heat from temperature. Ask them how heat is measured, and introduce the equation

$$heat = mass \times change\ in\ temperature \times specific\ heat$$

Solve problems using the equation, emphasizing proper units. Once students have mastered these, pose the problem: How much heat is needed to melt 10.0 grams of ice? Some of your students might recall the heat of fusion from the previous day.

Topic III *The Gas Laws (6 days)*

Goal: Can the behavior of gases be described mathematically?

Instructional Objectives

Students will be able to:
1. Use the kinetic theory of gases to explain gas behavior.
2. Solve problems using the gas laws.
3. Apply Avogadro's Hypothesis, Dalton's Law, and Graham's Law.
4. Explain the conditions that favor or inhibit ideal gas behavior.

Motivation for the Topic

Show how the water stays in a full glass as it is slowly raised from a basin of water. (See pages 30–31 of the text.) Develop the concept of gas pressure, and explore the units used to express it, including millimeters of mercury (mm Hg), atmospheres, and kilopascals.

Development of the Topic

Ask students how they picture the molecules in a gas and develop the kinetic theory of gases. Alternatively, the kinetic theory can be presented after the gas laws.

Use a bell jar over a pressure plate, with a vacuum pump, to show the effect of pressure change on gas volumes. Place two balloons, one filled with air, the other with water, in the bell jar, and then pump out the air. Have students try to figure out why one balloon gets larger. For fun, you might throw some marshmallows into the bell jar as well. The quantitative relationship between pressure and volume can be demonstrated with a Boyle's Law apparatus placed on an overhead projector. Have students graph the pressure vs. the volume, and present the concept of indirect variation. Develop the Boyle's Law equation, $P_1V_1 = P_2V_2$, at constant temperature, for a constant mass of gas. Provide several sample problems for practice.

Charles' Law can be demonstrated by stretching an uninflated balloon over a flask and placing the flask on a hot plate. Use a round balloon, not a long thin one! Present some sample T vs. V data, and have students plot the data. The plot should pass through the origin only if Kelvin temperature is used. Explain the significance of "absolute" temperature, and drill the conversion from Celsius to Kelvin temperature. Show that direct variation results in the relationship: $V_1/T_1 = V_2/T_2$. Present some sample problems, including some that require that the temperature be converted to Kelvin.

Show that the two gas laws can be combined into one expression

$$\frac{P_1V_1}{T_1} = \frac{P_2V_2}{T_2}$$

Solve problems using this combined gas law. Use kinetic theory to explain why the gas laws are valid and under what conditions they would not be valid. Define an ideal gas as one that obeys the gas laws. Have students predict the effect on the pressure and/or volume of changing the number of gas molecules in a system. State Avogadro's hypothesis.

At this time, you may wish to insert n into your combined gas law, or to go farther, introduce the gas constant R.

If you present the following problem: "A scientist pumps oxygen into a metal container to a pressure of 100. kP. He then adds neon until the total pressure is 150 kP. How much pressure is exerted by the neon gas?" students will come up with Dalton's Law on their own. They will also be able to correctly conclude that there must be only half as many neon molecules as oxygen molecules in the container.

Graham's Law can be qualitatively illustrated by dipping one cotton swab in concentrated HCl, and another in concentrated NH_3, and then holding them a few inches apart. The white cloud forms closer to the HCl, because the NH_3 diffuses faster. You can state the law simply as "The lighter gas moves faster." Should you wish to present the mathematical law of diffusion, be warned that even very gifted students have difficulty with an inverse, square root relationship.

TOPIC IV *Liquids and Solids (4 days)*

Goal: How are liquids and solids different from gases?

Instructional Objectives

Students will be able to:
1. Describe the properties of liquids and solids, as distinguished from those of gases.
2. Relate forces of attraction to vapor pressure, boiling point, rate of evaporation, and melting point.
3. Describe six types of phase change, and know which are exothermic, and which endothermic.
4. Compare and contrast the types of molecular motion in the three states.
5. Interpret phase diagrams. (Recommended)

Motivation for the Topic

Have an evaporation race. Soak three cotton balls, one in water, one in ethanol, and one in acetone. Have three students make streaks on the chalkboard simultaneously and observe which dries first. How do we explain and predict the properties of liquids?

Development of the Topic

Ask students to predict what happens when water is poured into a bottle, which is then sealed. Does the water continue to evaporate? Why does the water not disappear completely? Students generally think that the air is "full" of water. What does that mean? Develop the concept of phase equilibrium. Define vapor pressure, and have students predict how the vapor pressure of the three liquids tested earlier would compare. Ask which of the cotton balls felt the coldest to the touch, and elicit an explanation. Develop the relationship between temperature and vapor pressure, and illustrate by using vapor pressure curves of several different liquids on the same set of coordinates.

Use the vapor pressure curves to illustrate the relationship between external pressure and boiling point, and define the "normal boiling point" of a liquid. If you have a good enough pressure plate and pump, heat some water to about 90°C, place it in a bell jar on the pressure plate, and pump out the air. Keep the water boiling as long as you can; then open the bell jar, and pour the water on your hand. Why did the boiling water not burn you? Explain that if you had a strong enough pump, you could get the water to boil at a temperature of 0°C. Since boiling is endothermic, the water would then begin to freeze. Introduce the concept of sublimation, and illustrate on a phase diagram how sublimation occurs. Sublimation can be nicely demonstrated by gently heating solid iodine in a beaker with a watch glass over the top. Try placing an ice cube on the watch glass. The crystals that form due to deposition of the iodine vapor are very beautiful. You might also discuss the relationship between sublimation and odor— unless a solid produces some vapor, how would you be able to smell it?

Suggested Laboratory Activities

1. **Introduction to the Laboratory and Determination of Density**

   Students are instructed in the use of the balance and of a graduated cylinder. They then determine the density of a rubber stopper (between 1.2 and 1.4 g/mL) and a sample of salt water. This first period in the laboratory should also include a review of laboratory rules and safety regulations.

2. **Construction of a Cooling Curve for a Pure Substance**

   Paradichlorobenzene works very well, freezing at 53°C. Place a test tube containing a sample of paradichlorobenzene in boiling water until it reaches a temperature above 70°C. Then immerse the test tube in cold water, measuring the temperature every 30 seconds. Constant stirring produces the best results.

   Some teachers may not wish to use paradichlorobenzene because of its toxicity. It is possible to substitute water, using a salt-ice bath to lower the temperature of the water to below its freezing point.

3. **Determination of the Heat of Fusion of Water**

   Requires just a balance, a Styrofoam cup, ice, and a thermometer. The answers obtained should always come out lower than the book value, because of inadequate insulation, but it is useful to have the students figure that out.

4. **Collection and Examination of a Gas**

   CO_2 is recommended. Several different experiments are possible, including a rough determination of the room temperature density of CO_2. The opportunities for good laboratory experiences related to Chapter 1 are far greater than those related to the next two chapters, so students will generally continue to perform labs on "Matter and Energy" after they have begun Chapter 2.

Atomic Structure

INTRODUCTION

In recent years, some first-year chemistry programs have been omitting the discussion of sublevels, using configurations that specify the principal energy level only. This text will not follow that approach, since the structure of the Periodic Table is best explained through the use of sublevels. Given a Periodic Table, students have little difficulty in presenting a correct sublevel configuration for most elements.

Nevertheless, the chapter is constructed so as to permit teachers to give configurations in terms of principal energy levels. They may omit pages 85 to 97. The questions at the back of the chapter include several that are based only on the simpler electron configurations.

Day	Lesson for the Day	Text Pages	Homework
1	Early atomic theories	66 to 68	Pg. 72, Practice 2.1
2	How are atoms alike?	68 to 71	Pgs. 72–73, Practice 2.2–2.4
3	How do atoms differ?	71 to 76	Pgs. 74–75, Practice 2.5, 2.6; Pgs. 108–110, Chapter Review 3, 6, 8, 15, 16, 33
4	Where are the electrons?	76 to 82	Pg. 79, Practice 2.7, 2.8
5	The quantum model	82 to 85	Pg. 85, Practice 2.9, 2.10; Pg. 112, Constructed Response 3
6*–7*	Sublevels, orbitals, and spin	85 to 89	Pg. 109, Chapter Review 18, 22
8*–9*	Electron configurations	89 to 97	Pgs. 95–96, Practice 2.11–2.13; Pg. 99, Practice 2.14, 2.15; Pgs. 108–110, Chapter Review 1, 2, 10–13, 18–32; Pg. 112, Constructed Response 2 and 4
10	Properties determined by atomic structure—valence electrons, ionization energy, and electronegativity	97 to 103	Pgs. 108–110, Chapter Review 4, 9, 14, 17, 34–38; Pgs. 111–112, Constructed Response 1

*Lessons that would be skipped by teachers wishing to omit sublevels from the material. In the suggested homework for Lesson 9, omit questions 37 and 38 if sublevels are not covered.

Topic I Basic Atomic Structure (3 days)

Goal: How has our view of the atom changed?

Instructional Objectives

Students will be able to:
1. State and explain Dalton's atomic theory.
2. Describe Rutherford's gold leaf experiment, and explain its significance.
3. Use atomic number and mass number to calculate the number of electrons, protons and neutrons.
4. Calculate the average atomic mass from the masses and percent of the isotopes.

Motivation for the Topic

How small could I theoretically cut a piece of copper?

Compare a particulate view of matter with a continuous view of matter. Democritus believed there was a smallest particle, the atom.

Development of the Topic

Show how our picture of the atom has changed, beginning with the Dalton atom. Dalton based his theory largely on the law of definite proportions; show how the fact that each compound contains elements in a fixed ratio by mass is consistent with an indivisible atom. You might wish to point out that although the experimental evidence available to Dalton may have indicated the existence of indivisible atoms, it did not prove their existence. Atomic theory was not generally accepted for another 100 years.

Discuss Thomson's experiments with cathode ray tubes. It is a good idea to actually show a cathode ray tube of the type illustrated in Figure 2-1 on page 67 of the text. Students have a difficult time understanding what the slit does without actually seeing it. I use a Tesla coil to produce the narrow beam of light in the tube, but I move the students to the back of the room; the demonstration does produce some X-rays. If exposure to this radiation concerns you, you might consider doing the demonstration once, and videotaping it for future use.

Rutherford's gold leaf experiment should be thoroughly discussed. Consider using the "cyclone fence" analogy from page 69 of the text.

In discussing the general structure of the atom be sure to clearly distinguish between the mass number and the atomic mass. Students frequently confuse these, and think that they can obtain an atomic mass from the reference tables. Some teachers tell students to find the mass number by rounding off the atomic mass; I strongly advise against this. For example, applying this method to chlorine, one obtains a mass number of 36, which does not, in fact, correspond to a stable isotope of chlorine. Better to state that the mass number of a given isotope is not obtainable from the Periodic Table, and must be provided by the symbol.

Drill students in obtaining the number of electrons, protons, and neutrons, from a symbol with a mass number, such as ^{14}C.

Topic II Electron Configurations (2–3 days if sublevels are omitted, 5–7 days if they are included)

Goal: Where are the electrons?

Instructional Objectives

Students will be able to:
1. Explain how line spectra are produced.
2. Describe the electron in terms of orbitals and probability clouds.
3. Write and interpret electron configurations based on the principal energy level.
*4. Write and interpret subshell designations and orbital designations.

*Optional

Motivation for the Topic

Continuous vs. bright line spectrum: Ideally, a spectroscope should be set up to view the spectrum produced by a hydrogen lamp. If a hydrogen lamp is unavailable, a mercury lamp will do, to illustrate what is meant by a bright line spectrum. This should be contrasted with the continuous spectrum of white light. Inexpensive hand spectroscopes can be distributed to students so that they can see the two different kinds of spectra.

Point out that each color of light has a particular frequency, and each frequency corresponds to a certain, definite amount of energy. In the bright line spectrum, then, we see some energies but not others. The energy is quantized—limited to certain values.

Development of the Topic

I use musical instruments to illustrate the difference between quantized energies and continuous energies. A piano is quantized while a violin is continuous. A trombone is continuous while a clarinet is quantized. Bohr attempted to explain why hydrogen produces the observed bright line spectrum.

The Bohr model is presented, as shown on page 80 of the text. Each line in the spectrum corresponds to an electron "leap" from one orbit to another. I point out during this discussion that Bohr's "orbit" has been replaced by the newer term "energy level." Emphasize that the visible lines are just a small portion of the entire spectrum. A chart showing the spectra of electromagnetic radiation should be used to illustrate how higher energy transitions produce ultraviolet light, while lower energy transitions produce infrared.

Describe the bright line spectrum as the "fingerprint" of the element. Spectral colors for some elements that have visible flame tests can be demonstrated impressively as follows: Dissolve the salt in methanol, in an evaporating dish. Copper, lithium, sodium, and potassium salts seem to give the best results. **Carefully** light the alcohol. Gently stir occasionally, and the characteristic color produced by each element is visible in the flame of the burning alcohol. **(Make sure to take adequate, appropriate precautions to protect yourself and your students in the event that one of the evaporating dishes tips over.)**

The quantum mechanical model is developed from the work of de Broglie and Heisenberg. One way of presenting the Heisenberg uncertainty principle is to imagine a super-fast camera that could magnify an image sufficiently to make an electron visible. Heisenberg would say that no matter how fast the shutter speed, the electron would always appear as a blur. I also mention having seen a bumper sticker that read "Heisenberg might have slept here."

In presenting the concept of an orbital, it is important for the students to understand that the orbital does not indicate the path of the electron. It indicates a region in which there is a high probability of finding the electron. You may wish to use the "shortstop analogy" from page 87 of the text.

At this point you must decide whether you wish to teach sublevels. If not, then discuss shell capacities, $2n^2$, and drill the configurations of elements 1 to 18.

In presenting the four quantum numbers—shell, subshell, orbital, and spin—many teachers use the apartment building analogy. To locate a resident, you need to know what floor he or she lives on—the principal energy level or shell—and which apartment within the floor—the sublevel, or subshell. Just as apartment 3A is usually identical to apartment 2A, but one floor above it, the 3s sublevel is identical to the 2s sublevel, but is one energy level above it.

Each apartment contains a certain number of rooms—the orbitals. Apartment 3d is a five-room apartment on the third floor. Five-room apartments are very expensive, so apartment 4s, which has only one room, always fills first. You might ask students to come up with a rent formula that represents the correct order of fill and is based on the floor and number of rooms. When it comes to spin—we have a limit of two people to a room. Come up with your own idea of how the two people can have opposite "spin"! (Pauli exclusion principle)

Having presented your building, have your students gradually fill it. Refer to the s-block, p-block, and d-block on the Periodic Table. Students should note that the number of elements within a period that fills each of these blocks corresponds to the electron capacity of that sublevel. It is clear that the table contains 2 columns of elements on the left, 6 on the right, 10 in between, and 14 cut out at the bottom. When you get to the configuration of a carbon atom, present all the possibilities for the two $2p$ electrons, i.e., in the same orbital, in different orbitals, same spin, different spins. Use Hund's rule to find the correct configuration. Introduce the terms "paired" and "unpaired" electrons.

In an introductory course, students need not be required to produce a subshell designation directly from the atomic number. However, given a Periodic Table with the principal energy levels indicated, they should be able to provide the subshells, and indicate which orbitals are filled. For example, given that Fe is 2-8-14-2, students should be able to write the subshell designation, and predict that there are 4 unpaired electrons.

Topic III *Properties of Atoms (1–2 days)*

Goal: What are some properties we can predict on the basis of atomic structure?

Instructional Objectives

Students will be able to:
1. Define ionization energy, valence electrons, and electronegativity.
2. Determine the charge of an ion based on the number of electrons lost or gained.
3. Predict trends in ionization energy, electronegativity, and number of valence electrons based on atomic structure, and/or location in the Periodic Table.

Motivation for the Topic

React both magnesium and calcium with water. (Add some phenolphthalein to add some color to the demonstration, and to demonstrate that the Mg does react, however slowly.) Why does the Ca react so much more readily than the Mg? We can often explain the behavior of atoms on the basis of their atomic structures.

Development of the Topic

Establish that both Mg and Ca react by losing electrons. Which should lose electrons more easily? Define ionization energy as the energy needed to remove the most loosely held electron. Elicit the trends in ionization energy both across a period and down a group. How would ionization energy be related to the reactivity of a metal?

Compare the electron configuration of an ion to that of a neutral atom. Note that the metals of the first two groups form ions with the electron configurations of the noble gas elements.

Similarly define electronegativity as an attraction for electrons, and have students predict the trend, and then provide a table so that they can check their predictions.

Suggested Laboratory Activities

1. **Flame Tests**

   Students should test solutions containing calcium, barium, potassium, sodium, lithium, and strontium ions. If using nichrome wire, use a separate wire for the sodium. Once the wire is contaminated with sodium, the other flame tests are difficult to see. If you have sufficient wire, you can use just one wire for each solution. This provides the most consistent results, as long as the students do not mix them up! An unknown solution should be provided as well. I would advise not using calcium ion as the unknown.

2. **Spectral Analysis**

   Requires a class set of hand spectroscopes. (These are not expensive!) Provide as many of the following as possible: Hg lamp, Ne lamp, H_2 lamp, Na lamp, He lamp. (Do not identify the lamps.) Have students observe each of the lamps with their spectroscopes, and draw the line spectrum. Using a chart of bright line spectra of the elements, students will determine which lamp is which.

3 *Bonding*

INTRODUCTION

The text presents covalent bonding first, before ionic bonding. Teachers who prefer the alternate approach will find that they can quickly establish the two possibilities, and then assign pages 125 to 127, followed by a return to the beginning of the chapter.

In the discussion of covalent bonds we do refer to the sublevels, which some teachers omit from Chapter 2. The emphasis, however, is on valence electrons and dot structures. The determination of molecular geometry, and its relationship to molecular polarity, is a major focus of the chapter. We urge teachers to prepare and use three-dimensional molecular models to supplement the diagrams in the book. "Constructed Response" question 2, on page 153, is designed to illustrate the inadequacies of two-dimensional models.

Day	Lesson for the Day	Text Pages	Homework
1	Forces between atoms	114 to 118	Pg. 123, Practice 3.2, 3.4
2	Covalent bonds	118 to 122	Pg. 123, Practice 3.1, 3.3; Pg. 151, Chapter Review 12, 16
3	Ionic bonds	125 to 127	Pg. 127, Practice 3.5–3.6; Pgs. 148–151, Chapter Review 1, 2, 10, 19, 28
4–5	Molecular polarity, and geometry	130 to 135	Pgs. 135–136, Practice 3.7–3.8; Pgs. 150–152, Chapter Review 4, 11, 13, 20, 29
6	Intermolecular attractions	136 to 141	Pg. 141, Practice 3.9–3.11; Pgs. 151–152, Chapter Review 17, 26, 30–35
7	Types of solids	141 to 143, 124 to 125, 128 to 130*	Pgs. 143–144, Practice 3.12; Pgs. 150–152, Chapter Review 6–9, 13, 18, 22, 24, 27*

*Some teachers prefer to omit network solids from the unit.

TOPIC I *Bonds Between Atoms (3–4 days)*

Goal: How do atoms connect to other atoms?

Instructional Objectives

Students will be able to:
1. Define a covalent bond in terms of electron sharing.
2. Define an ionic bond in terms of electron transfer.
3. Draw dot structures for simple molecules.
4. Predict bond polarity or ionic character based on electronegativities.
5. Predict whether a given compound is ionic or covalent.

Motivation for the Topic

What do we mean when we refer to hydrogen as H_2? Alternate to begin with ionic bonding: burn a piece of magnesium ribbon, and ask what is happening, in terms of atomic structure.

Development of the Topic

Show the energy changes that occur as hydrogen atoms bond (Figure 3-2 on page 117). Emphasize that bond formation is always exothermic. Use a dot structure to illustrate the H_2 molecule, and explain the use of dot structures in representing molecules. Show how molecules such as Cl_2 and F_2 obey the "octet rule." Then permit the students to figure out how an N_2 molecule could form octets on the two nitrogen atoms. Illustrate other molecules with double and/or triple bonds. Point out that since these molecules contain bonds between identical atoms, the sharing of electrons in these molecules is *equal* sharing.

Elicit the dot structure of HF, and discuss the *unequal* sharing of electrons in that molecule. Define polar and nonpolar covalent bonds. Illustrate the use of electronegativity in predicting bond polarity. Have students draw dot structures for other simple molecules, such as H_2O, NH_3, CO_2, BrCl, CH_4, and SO_2.

Ask students to draw a dot structure for MgO. Have them check the difference in electronegativity, and ask them to predict what might happen when the difference is that large. Show how the resulting transfer of electrons produces ions, and illustrate how the resulting ions clump together to form an ionic solid. Discuss the general properties of ionic solids. The change in electrical conductivity that occurs upon melting can be demonstrated by heating ammonium nitrate in an evaporating dish, and inserting a conductivity apparatus. Show how dot structures of ionic substances differ from those of molecular substances.

Topic II *Molecular Structure (3–4 days)*

Goal: How do we predict the behavior of molecules?

Instructional Objectives

Students will be able to:
1. Identify common molecules as polar or nonpolar, dipoles or non-dipoles.
2. Predict geometry of simple molecules, and draw representative structures.
3. Predict whether a molecule is polar or nonpolar based on its geometry.
4. Describe intermolecular attractions, including London forces and hydrogen bonds.
5. Predict physical properties on the basis of intermolecular attractions.

Motivation for the Topic

Perform the experiment illustrated on page 130. I suggest that you use a rubber rod, rubbed with fur, to provide the negative charge. Unless it is a very cold, dry day it is difficult to demonstrate the attraction to a positively charged rod. Repeat the experiment with a nonpolar liquid such as pentane or perchlorethylene. (When I use perchlorethylene, I tell the students that it is CCl_4, because it is much easier for the them to see that CCl_4 is nonpolar.)

Development of the Topic

Use a molecular model to show that the sides of a water molecule have different charges and how the molecule would spin when a charged rod is brought near it. Define dipoles, or polar molecules, as molecules having two oppositely charged centers of charge. Illustrate why molecules such as CO_2 and CCl_4 are nonpolar. Ask students to predict the polarity of NH_3 and Cl_2, and use molecular models to verify their predictions. Emphasize that polarity depends upon geometry.

Show how geometry can be predicted by distributing electron pairs as far from each other as possible around a central atom. Illustrate why water is bent, ammonia is pyramidal, methane is tetrahedral, and carbon dioxide is linear. Show how the shape of one molecule can be found from the shape of another; e.g., H_2S should resemble water, PH_3 resembles ammonia, and CS_2 resembles CO_2.

Show that methane and butane are gases at room temperature. I use a butane lighter to make the point that butane is easily liquefied under pressure, but methane cannot be liquefied at room temperature. Why? Pentane and octane are liquids at room temperature. What is the apparent trend? Show the comparative boiling points within the noble gas and halogen elements. Conclude that intermolecular attractions are related to molecular size, and that generally, larger molecules, with more electrons, have stronger attractions. Define these intermolecular attractions as dispersion forces.

Construct a graph comparing the boiling points of H_2S, H_2Se, and H_2Te. (See text page 138, Figure 3-10.) Ask students to predict the boiling point of water on the basis of the graph. Why does water not follow the general trend? Show how hydrogen bonds are formed between adjoining water molecules. Illustrate the hydrogen bonding between the hydrogen on one molecule and small, highly electronegative elements (F, O, or N) on another molecule. Have students predict the relative boiling points of C_3H_8, C_3H_7OH, and $C_3H_5(OH)_3$, and explain their predictions.

Topic III *Types of Solids (1–2 days)*

Goal: How do we explain the bonding in the solid state?

Instructional Objectives

Students will be able to:
1. Distinguish among ionic, molecular, metallic, and network solids.
2. Compare the physical properties of the four types of solids.
3. Predict the type of solid based on a given formula, or a given set of properties.

Motivation for the Topic

Test the electrical conductivity of several metals, some ionic solids, and some molecular solids. Which of these samples conducts electricity? Compare the conductivity of a melted ionic solid with that of melted wax, or melted paradichlorobenzene. What type of solid conducts when melted? Why do these three types of solids have such different properties?

Development of the Topic

Contrast these three types of solids in terms of the nature of the bonding particles, the nature of the attractions between them, the strength of those attractions, and the resulting physical properties. Having the students construct a suitable chart is a good idea. Summarize by asking students to classify common substances; dry ice, brass, rust, aspirin, and wax are a few suggestions.

Network solids are comparatively rare, and some syllabi omit them. Should you wish to include this fourth type of solid, list the properties of diamond (solid *D* in Practice 3.12, page 143). Students will see that these properties fit none of the three solid types you have already discussed. Show how a chain of covalent bonds results in formation of diamond and graphite, and list the resulting properties. (Note: Graphite *does* conduct electricity, but most network solids do not.)

Suggested Laboratory Activity

Molecular Models

Students should use molecular models to construct models of a large number of simple molecules. On the basis of their models, they should be able to draw the dot structure for each molecule, and predict the polarity of the molecule.

Students can also be asked to construct molecular models using household materials, such as toothpicks and marshmallows. Assign fairly complicated molecules, such as acetone, benzene, or acetic acid, and see what they come up with.

4 Formulas and Equations

INTRODUCTION

After presenting the principles of chemical bonding, it is logical to use those principles to derive chemical formulas, and from there, to present and balance chemical equations, as is done in this chapter. An equally valid alternative approach is to move immediately to the Periodic Table (Chapter 5) and descriptive chemistry (Chapter 6), before teaching the mathematical work in Chapters 4 and 7. You must decide whether you wish to present all of the major mathematical topics at once, or to split them up.

The skills introduced in this chapter will be needed throughout the rest of the course. When teaching mole relationships, acid-base chemistry, solutions, and redox, you may wish to encourage students to revisit Chapter 4.

Day	Lesson for the Day	Text Pages	Homework
1	Binary formulas (ionic)	156 to 160	Pg. 159, Practice 4.1; Pg. 160, Practice 4.2
2	Polyatomic ions	160 to 161	Pgs. 161–162, Practice 4.3, 4.4
3–4	Molecular formulas	162 to 163	Pg. 163, Practice 4.5
5	Oxidation states	163 to 167	Pg. 165, Practice 4.6; Pg. 166, Practice 4.7, 4.8; Pg. 178, Constructed Response 2
6	Formula mass	167 to 169	Pg. 169, Practice 4.9
7	Chemical equations	169 to 172	Pg. 172, Practice 4.10; Pg. 178, Constructed Response 1
8–9	Types of reaction	172 to 176	Pg. 175, Practice 4.11; Pgs. 176–177, Practice 4.12

TOPIC I Formula Writing (3–4 days)

Goal: How do we write chemical formulas?

Instructional Objectives

Students will be able to:
1. When given the name, write a chemical formula using the Stock system.

2. When given the formula, provide the name of a compound, using the Stock system.
3. Write chemical formulas for molecular substances when given prefix names.
4. Give correct names for molecular substances, given the formula.
5. Distinguish between molecular and empirical formulas.

Motivation for the Topic

What is the formula for sodium chloride? (Students know that it is NaCl.) What is the formula for magnesium chloride? If a student answers correctly $MgCl_2$, ask how he or she knew. If, as happens most frequently, a student answers "$MgCl$," use atomic structure to illustrate that the Mg forms a 2+ ion, while the Cl forms a 1- ion. How can these ions form a neutral substance?

Development of the Topic

Show how a neutral compound is formed from Al^{3+} with O^{2-}. Once it is clear why Al_2O_3 is the simplest possible formula, introduce the "crisscross method" as a simple way of obtaining correct formulas.

Define a binary compound as a compound containing only two different elements, and have students notice (from magnesium chloride, aluminum oxide, and sodium chloride) how their names always end in "ide," and always list the metal ion first. Give the students several more formulas to do. Include calcium oxide, to point out that the charges are "crisscrossed" in lowest terms, so that it is CaO and not Ca_2O_2.

Burn a piece of steel wool in the flame of a gas burner, and show the students the resulting compound. (It should come out greenish in color.) What is the product when we burn Fe? Burning produces oxides. This oxide has the formula FeO. What is rust made of? Elicit that rust is also an oxide of iron—so why does it look so different from the burned steel wool? Refer students to a reference table, where they can see that iron has two common positive charges: 2+ and 3+. In rust, the iron is 3+. What formula would that give us? Chemists prefer that the names of compounds not be ambiguous. The same name cannot be given to two different compounds. To solve this problem, we use the Stock system of naming. Show that one of the oxides is iron(III) oxide, while the other is iron(II) oxide. Emphasize that the Roman numeral is the *charge* of the ion, and *not* the number of ions in the formula!

Have students figure out the formula of such compounds as iron(III) chloride, nickel(II) sulfide, and tin(IV) oxide. (Many students are likely to write Sn_2O_4 for the tin compound; remind them to crisscross in lowest terms. Ask students to correctly name FeS, Ni_2O_3, PbS_2, $CoCl_3$, and $ZnBr_2$. Ask the class, "Why don't we call the last of these zinc(II) bromide?"

Show the class a large blue crystal of copper(II) sulfate. How does this name differ from those we have discussed thus far? The *-ate* ending indicates a polyatomic ion. Define a polyatomic ion (introduced in Chapter 3) as a charged particle containing two or more atoms. Refer students to a table of polyatomic ions, so that they can discover the formula for the sulfate ion. Elicit the correct formula, $CuSO_4$. Ask students to write the formula for sodium sulfate, and then aluminum sulfate. Show why the formula of aluminum sulfate requires parentheses, and state the rule that parentheses are required to show more than one of any polyatomic ion. Drill, by asking students to write formulas for such compounds as calcium nitrate, iron(III) sulfate, nickel(II) phosphate, and aluminum hydroxide. Have students give the correct names for K_2CO_3, $ZnSO_3$, $Fe(NO_3)_3$, and Mg_3N_2. After having spent a period dealing with polyatomic ions students will often fail to correctly identify the nitride ion.

Ask students to name the compound CO_2. Compare this name with the name given to SnO_2. Why do we name these compounds differently? Remind students that the compounds of metals are generally ionic. Compounds lacking metals are generally molecular. Molecular compounds are named by using numerical prefixes. List the prefixes, from *mono-* to *hexa-*. Have students name the compounds NO_2, CCl_4, N_2O_3, and P_2O_5. Ask students to write the formula for dinitrogen tetraoxide. Emphasize that molecular formulas are not reduced to lowest terms. Remind them that glucose is $C_6H_{12}O_6$. Introduce the concept of the empirical formula as the simplest whole number ratio among the elements in the compound. What is the empirical formula of glucose?

Have students deduce the empirical formulas of $HC_2H_3O_2$, $H_2C_2O_4$, and H_2SO_4.

It is a good idea to spend at least one period having students practice formula writing and naming. Groups of four students can cooperatively complete a work sheet on the topic.

If you wish, you may point out that the compound with the formula NO is often referred to as nitric oxide. How else might it be named? One possibility is nitrogen monoxide. Another, using the Stock system, is nitrogen(II) oxide. In chemistry, then, there are three ways to say "NO!"

Topic II Oxidation Numbers (1 day)

Goal: How can we apply the Stock system to molecular substances?

Instructional Objectives

Students will be able to:
1. Find the oxidation state of the elements in simple compounds.
2. Find the oxidation states of the elements in polyatomic ions.

Motivation for the Topic

What name would you give to the compound SnI_4? (tin(IV) iodide) The electronegativity of I is 2.7, while that of Sn is 2.0. With an electronegativity difference of only 0.7, the compound is not ionic. In that case, what do we mean when we say that the Sn is +4? Chemists often find it useful to assign a whole number charge to atoms in compounds even when those compounds are not ionic. These numbers are called oxidation numbers, or oxidation states.

Development of the Topic

Define oxidation state as the charge an atom would acquire if all of its bonds were ionic. Illustrate how the oxidation states in a water molecule work out to +1 and –2. Point out that it is generally possible to assign oxidation states without using molecular structures, since many elements show only one oxidation state in their compounds, and the sum of the oxidation states in any compound must be zero.

List the rules given on page 162 of the text. Ask students to find the oxidation state of the N in KNO_3, the S in $BaSO_4$, and the C in Na_2CO_3. You might wish to solve these problems using the format illustrated at the bottom of page 162.

Ask students to find the oxidation state of the C in the carbonate ion, CO_3^{2-}. (They will usually get the wrong answer, +6.) Emphasize that the sum of the oxidation states in an ion must equal the charge of that ion. Show that the oxidation state of C in the carbonate ion is the same as the C in Na_2CO_3. The oxidation state of an element within a given polyatomic ion is always the same. It is often easiest to get an oxidation state by looking at the ion alone. What is the oxidation state of the Cl in $Al(ClO_3)_3$? You can solve this by showing that in order for the one Al^{+3}, the nine O^{-2}, and the three Cl to add up to zero, each Cl must be +5. It is much simpler to look at the chlorate ion, ClO_3^-, and see that with 3 oxygens at –2, the Cl must be +5 to add up to the charge of the ion, 1–.

Give the students ample opportunity to practice finding oxidation states. They will need to use this technique again in the redox chapter (Chapter 13).

Topic III Formula Mass (1 day)

Goal: What qualitative and quantitative information can be obtained from chemical formulas?

Instructional Objectives

Students will be able to:
1. Explain why a chemical formula contains both qualitative and quantitative information.

2. Find a formula mass, in amu, from a chemical formula.
3. Find a molar mass, in grams, from a chemical formula.

Motivation for the Topic

We know that a balloon filled with helium (He) gas will float, while one filled with carbon dioxide (CO_2) gas will sink. We say that He is "lighter than air," while CO_2 is "heavier than air." How can we use our knowledge of formulas and atomic masses to determine the mass of a molecule?

Development of the Topic

What is the mass of He? Our reference table tells us that He has an atomic mass of 4, so an average He atom has a mass of 4 amu. What is the mass of carbon dioxide? The formula tells us that there is one C, and there are 2 Os, in a CO_2 molecule. The mass of a molecule is the sum of the masses of its atoms. A CO_2 molecule has a mass of 44 amu. Of the molecules in air, 80 percent are nitrogen molecules, N_2. What is the molecular mass of nitrogen?

Remind students that ionic substances do not consist of molecules. Therefore, when we add up the masses the elements in their formulas, we are finding the *formula mass*. What is the formula mass of calcium carbonate ($CaCO_3$)? What is the formula mass of calcium nitrate? Note that we need to know how to write the formula before we can find the formula mass.

The amu is much too small a unit to be practical in ordinary situations. We normally measure the mass of chemicals in grams. Chemists have defined the *molar mass* as the sum of the masses of the elements in the formula, with the unit simply changed to grams. Thus the molar mass of water is 18 grams. What is the molar mass of CO_2? What is the molar mass of $CaCO_3$? Give plenty of examples.

Topic IV *Chemical Equations (3 days)*

Goal: How can we predict, write, and balance chemical equations?

Instructional Objectives

Students will be able to:
1. Balance simple chemical equations.
2. Identify the reactants and products in a chemical equation.
3. Illustrate the law of conservation of mass from a balanced chemical equation.
4. Identify various types of chemical reaction.
5. Given the reactants, predict the products and balance the resulting equation.

Motivation for the Topic

Place a piece of magnesium ribbon in a test tube containing 1 molar HCl. Have students describe what they see, and write "Magnesium + Hydrochloric acid." Allow students to predict, on the basis of what they see, what the products of the reaction might be, and write the word equation for the reaction, illustrating the reactants and products. How do chemists represent chemical equations?

Development of the Topic

Describe the equation above as a word equation, and point out that chemists generally prefer to write chemical equations that provide the chemical formula of the substances in the reaction. Write "Mg + HCl →" and allow the students to write the formula of hydrogen, H_2, and magnesium chloride, $MgCl_2$. We now have the equation $Mg + HCl → MgCl_2 + H_2$. Students will usually recognize that this equation is not balanced. Elicit from them what they mean by a balanced equation. Have a student balance the equation, and point out why it is advantageous to use balanced equations in chemistry. Show that in the balanced equation, the sum of all of the masses of the reactants equals the sum of all of the masses of the products.

Go over the techniques for balancing equations. (See text: pages 168–169.) Provide several examples, beginning with the simplest. Encourage students to begin to try numbers even if they do not immediately see the final answer.

Begin the following lesson by showing pieces of mossy zinc, and explaining that you intend to add these to a solution of sulfuric acid, H_2SO_4. (Be sure to use dilute sulfuric acid, about 1 molar.) Ask your students to predict what will happen. If they do not respond, refer them back to the previous day's demonstration with Mg and HCl. Illustrate that both of these are reactions between a metal and an acid. Similar reactions often produce similar results. Show that the zinc reacts with the acid to produce H_2 gas. It helps us to predict chemical changes, if we can classify reactions. For now, we will look at four types of chemical reaction.

Illustrate each of the four reaction types by performing the actual chemical reaction. Have students complete and balance each equation. The lesson is as much about practicing equation balancing as it is about classifying reactions. Suggested reactions include (in aqueous solution):

- Single replacement—zinc in copper sulfate, copper in silver nitrate, or aluminum in hydrochloric acid.
- Double replacement—silver nitrate and barium chloride, sodium iodide and lead(II) nitrate, or barium chloride and sodium chromate.
- Combination (also called composition, or synthesis)—burning hydrogen, burning Mg, or NH_3 + HCl gases. (Use concentrated HCl and concentrated NH_3, and just hold the two beakers next to each other.)

- Decomposition—add the catalyst MnO_2 to a sample of H_2O_2, or heat a sample of $CuSO_4 \cdot 5H_2O$ solid until it turns white (the water droplets are visible on the test tube).

Suggested Laboratory Activity

Types of Chemical Reactions

Have students perform several of each type of reaction, record their observations, and write balanced equations for the reactions.

The Periodic Table

INTRODUCTION

Chapter 5 deals with the Periodic Table and discusses the general trends that can be predicted using the table. Most teachers will probably want to cover all of Chapter 5.

Day	Lesson for the Day	Text Pages	Homework
1	History of the table	181 to 186	
2	General trends	186 to 190	Pgs. 190–191, Practice 5.1–5.3
3–4	Bonding behavior	191 to 195	Pgs. 198–199, Constructed Response 1–4; Pgs. 196–198, Chapter Review

Topic 1 Using the Periodic Table to Predict the Behavior of Elements (3–4 days)

Goal: How is the Periodic Table used to predict chemical behavior?

Instructional Objectives

Students will be able to:
1. Explain the general organization of the Periodic Table in terms of Periods and Groups.
2. Predict trends in ionization energy, electronegativity, valence electrons, and chemical properties within Groups and Periods.
3. Contrast the behavior of metals with the behavior of nonmetals.

Motivation for the Topic

Why does the Periodic Table look the way it does? Mendeleev grouped the elements in order by their mass, but why did he start a new period when he went from fluorine to sodium? (Neon had not been discovered yet!) What does the mass of an element have to do with its chemical behavior?

Development of the Topic

Discuss the early history of the table. (See pages 181–186.) Show how the mass of argon would place it in Group 1 when elements are grouped by mass. Have the students realize that the success of the early Periodic Table was despite the erroneous assumption that the chemical properties of the elements were determined by their mass.

Have students predict the trends in atomic radius, and illustrate these trends using graphs such as Figure 5-1. You may wish to ask the students to graph the radius within a Group or Period, assigning different Groups and Periods to different students. Similarly, elicit and graph the ionization energies within Groups and Periods. If you have taught sublevels in Chapter 2, you can explain the two dips in the graph across a Period; the first occurs because p orbitals are repelled by the s orbitals in their energy level. It is thus easier to remove an electron from boron, $1s^2 2s^2 2p^1$, than it is from beryllium, $1s^2 2s^2$. The second dip occurs when a second electron is added to one of the p orbitals; the repulsion between the two electrons makes it easier to remove one of them.

Demonstrations comparing the activities of the metals of Groups 1 and 2 can be done at this time; the students should be able to predict the behavior of potassium in water once they have seen what sodium does. Be sure to use very small pieces of these metals and cold water. For safety reasons, do not have a student help you with the sodium and potassium demonstrations; students can safely react magnesium and calcium with water. Use phenolphthalein to enhance the visibility of the reactions, especially with the magnesium.

Students should become acquainted with the "colorful" behavior of the transition metals. Some pretty demonstrations that illustrate this behavior include:

- Add concentrated NH_3 solution to a solution of $CuSO_4$; then add concentrated HCl.
- Prepare an acidic (use dilute H_2SO_4) solution of $KMnO_4$, and pour it into a beaker containing a solution of either Na_2SO_3 or any Sn^{2+} salt. The color change is dramatic.

6 **Some Chemical Families**

INTRODUCTION

Chapter 6 discusses the specific properties of elements in several groups within the table. Most teachers will probably pick a few representative Groups from Chapter 6. That is the approach taken in this guide, choosing to study Groups 1, 2, and 17.

Day	Lesson for the Day	Text Pages	Homework
1	Group 1 metals	200 to 205	Pg. 205, Practice 6.1–6.5
2	Group 2 metals	205 to 210	Pg. 211, Practice 6.6–6.9
3	Group 17	225 to 229	Pg. 231, Practice 6.14; Pgs. 231–233, Chapter Review 1–6, 13–20, 22, 24, 25; Pg. 234, Constructed Response 1 a, b, c, e and 4

Topic I *Behavior of Some of the Groups (3 days)*

Goal: How can we predict and explain the behavior of the elements in Groups 1, 2, and 17? (You may choose to emphasize other groups, of course!)

Instructional Objectives

Students will be able to:
1. Classify elements as alkali metals, alkaline earth metals, or halogens.
2. Illustrate how the behavior of the elements within these Groups follows predictable patterns.
3. Write chemical equations for some of the important reactions of these elements.
4. Given the behavior of one element in a Group, predict the behavior of another element in that Group.

Motivation for the Topic

Ancient peoples knew elements such as gold, silver, and copper. Sodium, a far more abundant element, was not isolated until 1807. Potassium, calcium, and magnesium were also purified for the first time in the early nineteenth century. Why were these elements so difficult to isolate?

Development of the Topic

Demonstrate the physical and chemical properties of the selected Groups. If you have not done so already (described in previous lesson), show the reactions of Ca, Mg, Na, and K in water. Begin with Mg, in a test tube containing water and some phenolphthalein. A faint pink color shows that the Mg does react, but very slowly. Students should then be able to predict the reactions of the other three metals, based on their atomic structure, radius, and ionization energy. (The sodium and potassium should be reacted in battery jars, not test tubes. Proper safety precautions should be taken.) Have students also predict the activity of Al compared with that of Mg, and demonstrate that Al does not react noticeably with cold water.

Have students write and balance the chemical equations for the reactions of the metals with water.

Provide two samples of water, one contaminated with a high concentration of calcium ions. (Do not tell the students which is which.) Provide soap, and have two students try to wash their hands in the two solutions. Discuss what is meant by "hard" water. (What is a three letter word meaning "hard water"? [Ice!])

Demonstrate some of the properties of chlorine, bromine, and iodine. Have students note the state and color of these three halogens, and review why the states are different. Antimony powder bursts into flame when sprinkled into a jar of chlorine gas. Steel wool, once ignited, burns impressively in chlorine as well. Both of these demonstrations are best performed in a hood.

The relative activities of these halogens can also be demonstrated by performing the replacement reactions, using chlorine water, bromine water, iodine, NaCl, NaBr, and NaI. Demonstrate the color of each reagent in perchlorethylene, or some other organic solvent. Then react the chlorine water with the NaI and NaBr, adding perchlorethylene to each test tube. The characteristic colors of the bromine and iodine will form in the organic layer. Repeat with bromine water in NaCl and NaI. Ask students to predict the results. (The bromine replaces the iodide, but does not react with the chloride ion.)

Suggested Laboratory Activities

1. **Activity Series**

   Students can compare the reactions of Ca and Mg with water, and then compare the reactions of Mg and Al with dilute acid. On this basis they can predict the relative activities of these three metals. Using replacement reactions, they can then compare the activities of Pb, Cu, and Ag. Ask students: Why were the first three metals discovered around 1807 while the last three were known since ancient times? What do you predict will happen if you add Al to solutions containing ions of these three metals? Have your students test their prediction and write balanced equations for all reactions that occur.

2. Transition Metals

Provide the opportunity for the students to perform some of the many colorful reactions of transition metal ions. These are fun, and also give the students the opportunity to practice writing and balancing equations. Some suggestions are

- Na_2CrO_4 (*aq*) with dilute H_2SO_4, then with NaOH
- Na_2CrO_4 (*aq*) with dilute H_2SO_4, then with $FeSO_4$ or $SnCl_2$
- $KMnO_4$ (*aq*) with dilute H_2SO_4, then with $SnCl_2$
- $Fe(NO_3)_3$ (*aq*) with NH_4SCN
- A solution of $CoCl_2$ in ethanol, with dilute $AgNO_3$

7 Chemical Calculations

INTRODUCTION

This is an area in which there is much variation among chemistry programs, in both scope and vocabulary. Some programs omit the molar volume of gases, some omit mass-mass problems, and some omit empirical formula problems. Should teachers refer to 18 grams as the molar mass of water, the gram-molecular mass, or the gram-formula mass? In this text all three terms are introduced, but I prefer molar mass.

All of the problem types listed above have been included, but those topics that are most frequently covered have been placed at the front of the chapter. Teachers wishing to omit molar volume, mass-mass, and the use of the Avogadro number in problem solving can assign only up to page 253, using the Chapter Review questions from 1 to 14 only. The 7-day calendar below is provided for these teachers.

Day	Lesson for the Day	Text Pages	Homework
1	Expressing quantity	235 to 239	Pg. 239, Practice 7.1–7.3
2	Percent composition	240 to 243	Pg. 243, Practice 7.4–7.5
3	Empirical formula	243 to 244	Pg. 244, Practice 7.6
4	Empirical formula from percent composition*	244 to 247	Pg. 247, Practice 7.7, 7.8
5	Molecular formula	247 to 249	Pgs. 249–250, Practice 7.9, 7.10*, 7.11, 7.12*
6	Mole to mole problems	250 to 252	Pgs. 252–253, Practice 7.13–7.14, 7.15
7	Problem practice	277 to 278	Pgs. 277–278, Chapter Review 1–9, 11–14

* If many of your students have weak math skills, you may wish to skip this topic. If you do, then omit the starred questions.

We continue the calendar of lessons now, for those wishing to take the more traditional and more inclusive approach.

Day	Lesson for the Day	Text Pages	Homework
8–9	Molar volume of gases, and mole conversions	253 to 258	Pg. 256, Practice 7.16–7.18
10	Gas densities	259	Pg. 259, Practice 7.19–7.21

Day	Lesson for the Day	Text Pages	Homework
11	Mass-mass problems	260 to 262	Pg. 262, Practice 7.22–7.24
12	Mass-volume and volume-volume problems	262 to 267	Pgs. 264–265, Practice 7.25–7.27; Pg. 267, Practice 7.28, 7.29
13	Practice and drill	277 to 280	Pgs. 278–280, Chapter Review 15–38

Beyond these topics, the "Taking a Closer Look" section in this chapter is quite extensive, and should be particularly useful to those wishing to prepare students for national examinations such as the SAT II.

Topic I Moles and Masses (2–3 days)

Goal: How do we use the relationship between moles and grams?

Instructional Objectives

Students will be able to:
1. Recognize that the term *moles* expresses the number of items, while the term *grams* expresses the mass of the items.
2. Convert from moles to grams and grams to moles for a given substance.
3. Find a percent composition from a given formula.

Motivation for the Topic

The neighborhood fruit store is selling apples for $1.00 per pound. How much would two dozen apples cost? What additional information do you need to answer this question? Suppose that a dozen of these apples weighs 5 pounds. Now how much would two dozen apples cost? In chemistry, as in everyday commerce, we often need to convert between the number of items, i.e., dozens, and the mass of the items. In chemistry, though, we do not use pounds; we use grams—and instead of "dozens," we express the number of particles using moles.

Development of the Topic

To solve the apple problem, we needed to know the mass of a dozen apples. To find the mass of a given number of moles of a substance, we need to know the mass of 1 mole of that substance. The mass of a mole is easy to find. We already know how to find the formula mass of a substance (Chapter 4). The mass of a mole is simply the formula mass in grams. We call the mass of 1 mole of a substance its gram-formula mass, or more simply, its molar mass.

Having defined molar mass, present some simple problems in determining it. Have students calculate the molar masses of water, carbon dioxide, and nitrogen gas, for example. Emphasize the correct unit, grams, or grams per mole. Once your students are confident that they can find the mass of 1 mole of a substance, ask them to find the mass of 2.0 moles of water. They should see that they can find the mass of any number of moles of a substance, using the relationship

$$moles \times molar\ mass = grams$$

Provide a few simple problems of this type.

Next, ask how many moles of water there are in 36 grams of water. Elicit the alternative form of the equation above:

$$\frac{moles}{molar\ mass} = grams$$

Provide several simple problems that involve converting to and from moles. I would suggest that at this time you give the students the molar masses, so that they can confidently get the correct answers. It is often best to isolate the one skill you are teaching in that lesson; once the students show a firm command of that skill, you can combine it with other skills.

The concept of percent composition can be introduced using the example on page 240, of the percent of girls in the class. If you wish to include a "real-world connection" in your approach, you might compare the percent iron in the three iron ores, Fe_2O_3 (hematite), Fe_3O_4 (magnetite), and FeS (pyrite). Which of these contains the greatest mass of iron per kilogram? What is the percent Fe in iron(II) oxide, FeO?

It is a good idea when giving sample percent composition problems to have students find the percent compositions of both glucose, $C_6H_{12}O_6$, and formaldehyde, CH_2O. Why did both come out the same?

When solving problems involving the percent of water in a hydrate, you might point out that the school buys its chemicals by the kilogram. When the school buys $CuSO_4 \cdot 5H_2O$ it is paying good money for ordinary water! What percent of the mass of this substance is actually water?

Topic II Empirical and Molecular Formulas (2 or 3 days, depending on whether you choose to include item 4 below)

Goal: How do we find empirical and molecular formulas of unknown substances?

Instructional Objectives

Students will be able to:
1. Define empirical formula as the simplest whole number ratio among the elements in the compound.

2. Recognize that only empirical formulas, and not molecular formulas, are obtainable from percent composition alone.
3. Determine the empirical formula from a given molecular formula.
4. Determine the empirical formula from percent composition.
5. Determine the molecular formula, when given the empirical formula and the molar mass.

Motivation for the Topic

Once we learned how to convert from moles to grams, we were immediately also able to convert from grams to moles. We have just learned how to find the percent composition from the molecular formula. (Review the percent composition of glucose and formaldehyde.) Can we find the molecular formula from the percent composition?

Elicit that we cannot determine the molecular formula from percent composition alone because two different molecules can have the same percent composition. Both glucose and formaldehyde have the same percent composition and the same empirical formula. We can determine only the empirical formula from the percent composition.

Development of the Topic

Because mole conversions have been introduced already, students can now use moles to help solve empirical formula problems. Begin by assuming that you have 100. grams of the substance in question. Then the number of grams of each element in the substance is equal to its percent composition. Show that we can convert the number of grams of each element in our 100.-gram sample to moles. We then express the empirical formula as the simplest whole number ratio among the moles we calculated.

Students will generally have little difficulty in finding the numbers of moles. If you tell them, for example, that the compound is 81.82% carbon and 18.18% hydrogen, they will generally find that there are 6.818 moles of carbon to 18.18 moles of hydrogen. But what is the simplest whole number ratio between those two numbers?

The usual method is to divide both numbers by the smallest. This gives us 1.000 C and 2.666 H. Will most of your students be able to see that this produces a ratio of 3 to 8? My recommendation is that, except as extra credit, empirical formula problems should be kept as simple as possible. $CaCO_3$, CH_4, CH_3, H_2SO_3 are suggested compounds to assign.

Once we have found the empirical formula, what extra information would enable us to find the molecular formula? Show that the molar mass of a molecule must be an exact multiple of the molar mass of its empirical formula. For example, the mass of glucose, 180, is exactly 6 times the mass of its empirical formula, CH_2O. (What do chemists call "CH_2O"? "Sea water"?) Use the method shown on page 248 of the text to show how a molecular formula is determined from empirical formula and molar mass.

Suggested substances for practice problems include butane, empirical formula C_2H_5, molar mass = 58; cyclohexane, empirical formula CH_2, molar mass = 84.

Topic III *Mole to Mole Problems (1–2 days)*

Goal: How can we use a balanced chemical equation to predict quantities?

Instructional Objectives

Students will be able to:
1. Express a balanced equation in terms of the mole ratios of the reacting species.
2. Given the number of moles of any substance in a balanced equation, compute the number of moles reacting with, or produced by, that number of moles.

Motivation for the Topic

Present a balanced equation, and ask the students what the balanced equation means. For example, what do we mean when we say, "Two hydrogens react with one oxygen to form two waters"? Establish that the units implied in the statement are molecules, or moles.

Development of the Topic

Begin with a problem that uses the same number of moles as shown in the coefficients of the balanced equation. For example, "How many moles of hydrogen react with one mole of nitrogen in the equation: $N_2 + 3\ H_2 \rightarrow 2\ NH_3$?" Then ask, "How many moles of hydrogen would be needed to produced 4 moles of NH_3?" Establish a method for solving "mole to mole" problems. My own experience is that most students prefer the "alternate method" on page 251 of the text.

Topic IV *Problems Involving Ideal Gases (3 days)*

Goal: How do we use mole relationships to deal with volumes of ideal gases?

Instructional Objectives

Students will be able to:
1. Identify 22.4 liters as the volume of 1.00 mole of any ideal gas at STP.
2. Convert liters to moles, grams, and number of particles, and vice versa.
3. Calculate the density of a given gas at STP from its molar mass, and vice versa.

Motivation for the Topic

Review Avogadro's Hypothesis. Establish that under the same conditions, equal volumes of different gases contain the same number of particles. Therefore, at STP, for a given number of gas particles, there must be just one volume these particles can occupy, no matter what the gas. For one mole, that volume at STP is 22.4 liters. If we can find the volume of one mole, then we can find the volume of any number of moles.

Development of the Topic

Having established that the volume of one mole is 22.4 L, ask your students to compute the volume of 2.0 moles of neon gas at STP. Derive the relationship

$$moles \times 22.4 \text{ L/mol} = liters$$

Pose problems in both directions, both moles to liters and liters to moles. Once students have mastered the conversion, remind them that they now know three quantities that are equivalent to one mole of a gas at STP: 22.4 liters, the molar mass, and 6.02×10^{23} molecules. Use the flow chart on page 256 to illustrate conversions among moles, volume, mass, and number of particles. Assign simple two-step problems, such as:

- What is the mass of 44.8 liters of O_2 at STP?
- What is the volume of 22.0 grams of CO_2 at STP?

Remind students that

$$moles = g/molar\ mass, \text{ and } moles = L/22.4.$$

$$\text{Therefore, } g/molar\ mass = L/22.4.$$

This equation can be rearranged to give

$$g/L = molar\ mass/22.4.$$

Elicit that g/L is a unit of density (D). Thus $D = molar\ mass/22.4$ L. Work through some problems going from molar mass to density and then from density to molar mass. Once students have mastered the relationship, you might try assigning this problem: A gas that has a density at STP of 2.5 g/L has the empirical formula CH_2. What is the molecular formula of the gas?

Topic V *Mass and Volume Relationships in Balanced Equations (2 days)*

Goal: How can we calculate the mass and volume of materials within a chemical reaction?

Instructional Objective

Students will be able to:

Given the mass, volume, or number of moles of any one substance in a balanced chemical reaction, compute the mass, volume, or number of moles of any other substance in the reaction.

Motivation for the Topic

Demonstrate that you can generate CO_2 gas by reacting dilute HCl with $CaCO_3$. Present the balanced equation for the reaction. Hold up a 1.00-liter soda bottle and ask, "How many grams of $CaCO_3$ would I need to react to fill this bottle with CO_2 gas at STP?" Establish that the students already know enough to be able to solve this problem. They have learned how to convert 1.00 liter into moles, how to convert moles of CO_2 to moles of $CaCO_3$, and how to convert moles to grams. Therefore, within any balanced equation, they should be able to find moles, grams, or liters of any ideal gas, from the given quantity of any other substance in the reaction. (You might want to point out that we are always assuming that any unspecified quantities of reactants are in excess.)

Development of the Topic

Begin with a simple problem, such as $2\,CO + O_2 \rightarrow 2\,CO_2$. How many grams of CO are needed to react with 44.8 liters of oxygen at STP? Emphasize that this is a three-step problem. The steps are (1) liters into moles, (2) moles to moles, (3) out of moles to grams. Provide a simple mass-mass problem, and a simple mass-volume problem.

Once the method is firmly established, present a problem like this one: In the reaction $N_2 + 3\,H_2 \rightarrow 2\,NH_3$, what volume of H_2 gas is needed to react with 10.0 liters of N_2 gas? Your students are likely to apply the three-step method they have learned. Allow them to do so, and then show them that they divided by 22.4 in step 1, and then multiplied by 22.4 in step 3, so the steps canceled out. Show them that in volume-volume problems, a one-step solution is possible: 10.0 liters of $N_2 \times 3H_2/N_2 = 30.0$ L. (Or, liters over coefficient = liters over coefficient.)

It is advisable to spend at least one additional day having students apply these techniques to several problems. Cooperative groups work particularly well in this area.

Suggested Laboratory Activities

1. **Determination of the Percent of Water in a Hydrate**

   Hydrated copper sulfate, $CuSO_4 \bullet 5\,H_2O$, works well. In addition to having students calculate the percent water in the hydrate, it is useful to have them calculate the number of water molecules in the formula.

They can convert the grams of water to moles, convert the grams of anhydrous crystal to moles, and then find the ratio.

2. Determination of the Formula of a Carbonate

This is very simple and easily doable in a 40-minute period. Students are given a sample of a carbonate or bicarbonate. Possible unknowns could be $NaHCO_3$, Na_2CO_3, K_2CO_3, and $BaCO_3$. Students weigh a sample into an Erlenmeyer flask. They then prepare a beaker of dilute HCl (the quantity and concentration of the HCl must be more than sufficient to completely convert the carbonate into CO_2) and find the mass of the beaker, HCl, flask, and carbonate together. The contents of the beaker are then poured into the flask, which is gently swirled until the reaction is complete. The flask and beaker are weighed again. The mass lost is carbon dioxide. Students can then find the moles of carbon dioxide, calculate the moles of carbonate, and, dividing grams by moles, determine the molar mass of their carbonate. They can then identify their particular carbonate.

3. Determination of the Molar Volume of a Gas

There are several methods that work well, but they do require students to convert volumes to STP, and if accurate answers are desired, to include a vapor pressure correction. One method is the reaction of Mg ribbon with dilute HCl in a gas-measuring tube. If gas-measuring tubes are unavailable, an ordinary graduated cylinder will do. Fill a trough with water. Add 10.0 mL of 6.0 M HCl to a 50.0-mL graduated cylinder, and then fill the cylinder to the top with water. Do not stir or shake the mixture. Use Mg strips of approximately 0.030 g. If there are not enough balances available capable of giving accurate readings to the nearest milligram, the strips can be preweighed by the instructor. Once the strips have been weighed, they should be curled into a ball, and placed in the previously prepared graduated cylinder. A glass plate is used to quickly invert the cylinder, and place it in the trough. The glass plate is removed, while the Mg stays in the cylinder. Once the acid diffuses down the cylinder, it will react, producing H_2 gas. The moles of H_2 are equal to the moles of Mg. The volume of H_2 collected, after it is corrected to STP, divided by the moles, should be 22.4 liters. (Remind the students not to touch the liquid in the trough once the reaction begins, and to rinse the trough thoroughly when they are done!)

Solutions

INTRODUCTION

The treatment of the qualitative and quantitative aspects of solubility seems pretty standard. Nearly all curricula will include the nature of the dissolving process, solubility curves, and concentration calculations. Optional topics include quantitative problems using colligative properties, Raoult's Law, and the relationship between the vapor pressure change and the changes in boiling point and freezing point.

This chapter introduces the concept of entropy. Students frequently ask, "What is stronger, the interionic attraction (in KCl, for example), or the ion-dipole attraction?" The answer is the interionic attraction. They now ask, "Then why does KCl dissolve?" The answer to this question involves entropy!

Day	Lesson for the Day	Text Pages	Homework
1	How do solutions form?	283 to 287	Pg. 316, Chapter Review 1
2	Like dissolves like	287 to 289	Pg. 288, Practice 8.1; Pg. 289, Practice 8.2, 8.3
3–4	Solubility curves and saturation	289 to 293	Pg. 292, Practice 8.4; Pg. 293, Practice 8.5–8.9; Pg. 319, Chapter Review 24–27
5	Factors that influence solubility	294 to 296	Pg. 296–297, Practice 8.10–8.13
6–7	Units of concentration	297 to 306*	Pg. 299, Practice 8.14–8.16, Pg. 302, Practice 8.17–8.19, Pg. 304, Practice 8.20–8.23, Pg. 306,* Practice 8.24, 8.25
8	Properties of solutions	306 to 313**	Pg. 313, Practice 8.26, 8.27** Pgs. 318–319, Chapter Review 22, 28–30

*Teachers who do not intend to present a quantitative treatment of colligative properties may choose to omit the discussion of molality and can end the reading assignment at page 304.
**Pages 310 to 311 deal with the quantitative treatment of colligative properties.

Topic 1 *The Dissolving Process (2 days)*

Goal: How do solutions form?

Instructional Objectives

Students will be able to:
1. Describe solutions as homogeneous mixtures.
2. Explain the dissolving process on the basis of bond breaking and bond formation.
3. Predict solubility on the basis of bonding forces; i.e., "Like dissolves like."
4. Distinguish the solute and solvent in different types of solutions.

Motivation for the Topic

Dissolve a small amount of sugar in a beaker of water. Ask students what happened to the sugar. Establish that water taken from the top of the beaker is just as sweet as water taken from the bottom. Dissolve a colored solute, such as sodium chromate (Na_2CrO_4). (Be sure to use a small enough amount of solute to produce an obviously homogeneous result.) Have students diagram what they think is the distribution of the particles in the solution.

Development of the Topic

Establish that a solution is a homogeneous mixture, and introduce the terms *solute* and *solvent*. Provide examples of solutions using each of the three phases as solutes, and using each of the three phases as solvents. Explain why a true aqueous solution is transparent. (You may wish to discuss why homogenized milk is not a true solution; the particles are large enough to block light.)

Illustrate the bond-breaking and bond-forming steps in the dissolving of NaCl in water. (See text page 286.) Show the ion-dipole attractions in the hydrated salt solution. Point out that a strong ion-dipole attraction is necessary for an ionic solid to dissolve. Water, because it is very highly polar, is able to dissolve many ionic solids.

In the second lesson, with the aim "How can we predict solubility?" demonstrate the solubility of I_2, $KMnO_4$, $NiCl_2$, and pentane, in water and in perchlorethylene. Establish that water is polar, while perchlorethylene is nonpolar. Lead students to the conclusion that ionic substances dissolve in highly polar solvents, while nonpolar, molecular substances dissolve in nonpolar solvents. Have students predict which solutes will dissolve in pentane. If it does not violate school rules, bring in a bottle of vodka, and ask students what the main ingredients are. (If it is 80 proof, it is about 40 percent ethanol and 60 percent water.) (If this violates school rules, the bottle could be empty or filled with water.) Why is ethanol miscible with water? Show that ethanol is highly polar. Polar solutes dissolve best in polar solvents—like dissolves like. (You might choose to show that ethanol is a much better solvent for iodine than is water. While ethanol is polar, it is not as highly polar as water, and can therefore dissolve some nonpolar solutes.)

I also suggest the following demonstration. Prepare a very dilute solution of I_2 in perchlorethylene and pour a small amount into a large test tube. Pour an aqueous solution of $CuSO_4$ on top of that. Ask students to predict what will happen if you pour in some pentane. (You can use toluene instead of pentane if you wish.) The solution now has three layers, red, blue, and white. Ask what will happen when you shake the solution. You end up with two layers. Then, by either adding more pentane, to make the organic layer float, or more perchlorethylene, to make the organic layer sink, you can get the layers to shift several times.

Topic II Factors That Influence Solubility (3–4 days)

Goal: How can we change the solubility of a given solute in a given solvent?

Instructional Objectives

Students will be able to:
1. Define saturated, unsaturated, and supersaturated solutions.
2. Explain the nature of a saturated solution both qualitatively, in terms of equilibrium, and quantitatively, as a solution containing a maximum amount of that solute, in that amount of solvent, at a given temperature.
3. Use solubility curves to make predictions about solutions at various temperatures and concentrations.
4. Compare the effects of changes in pressure and temperature on the solubility of most solids and gases in water.

Motivation for the Topic

Display a beaker containing a saturated solution of sucrose, with a large excess of sucrose on the bottom. Show that the solid does not dissolve upon stirring, and ask why it does not. Students may tell you that the solution is saturated, or that it is "full." Ask them what they mean, and then ask what would happen if you added some other solute, such as sodium chromate (or any other highly colored, highly soluble salt). Show that the salt dissolves readily in the water.

Development of the Topic

Explain saturation in terms of equilibrium. Ask students how a solution could be tested to see whether it is unsaturated. Add a crystal of sodium chromate to an unsaturated solution of sodium chromate; explain that we know that the solution is unsaturated because the crystal dissolves. What would have happened had the solution been saturated?

Take a preprepared, supersaturated solution of either sodium acetate or sodium thiosulfate and ask a student to test it to see whether it is saturated. When the rapid crystallization occurs, make sure that the student also notices that the solution gets hot. (Instant heat packs often work this way.) Define a supersaturated solution, and explain how such a solution is prepared. Emphasize that supersaturated solutions cannot be prepared by adding additional solute to a saturated solution. They are prepared only by gradual cooling of a saturated solution. Also emphasize that supersaturated solutions are rare. Most saturated solutions form crystals when they are cooled. (You can demonstrate this using potassium chlorate; a saturated solution at 100°C forms beautiful crystals as it is cooled—it appears to "snow" inside the test tube.)

Place your beaker of saturated sucrose solution on a hot plate and ask students to predict the results. Elicit that temperature often has a large effect on solubility, and provide access to a set of solubility curves. (See text page 290.) Emphasize that each curve represents a saturated solution. Provide several sample problems using the solubility curves. A second day may be needed to practice problems using solubility curves, particularly if you wish to include problems in which the mass of water is not 100 grams.

If your solubility curves include some gaseous solutes, such as NH_3 or HCl, ask why these decrease in solubility with increasing temperature. Point out that gases typically become less soluble at higher temperatures. Adding phenolphthalein to a 1.00 M NH_3 solution, and then heating the solution on a hot plate can demonstrate this. The color begins to fade, as the increased temperature drives ammonia out of the water.

Show a bottle of colorless carbonated beverage (lemon-lime soda or mineral water). Have students observe that there is no bubbling until the cap is removed. Relate this observation to the change in pressure that occurs when the cap is removed. Establish that gases are most soluble at high pressures and low temperatures. A discussion of scuba diving and "the bends" is relevant here.

Topic III *Expressing Concentration (2–3 days)*

Goal: How can we precisely indicate the concentration of a solution?

Instructional Objectives

Students will be able to:
1. Calculate molarity from moles and volume, or moles from molarity and volume.
2. Given the mass of a solute and the volume of the solution, calculate molarity.

3. Calculate the mass of solute needed to produce a given molarity in a given volume.
4. Determine concentrations in parts per million, given percent by mass, or given the mass of the solute and of the solution.
5. Solve dilution problems using molarity.

Motivation for the Topic

In advance, prepare two cups of tea, in separate beakers or glass cups. Make one extremely dilute, and the other quite concentrated. Show these to the class, pointing out that they were both made with the same brand of tea. Why are they different? What are the chemical terms we use instead of "strong" and "weak"? Point out that "dilute" and "concentrated" or "strong" and "weak" are inexact terms. How can we express a precise concentration?

An alternate motivation is to pour samples of HCl into test tubes from two different bottles of HCl, one concentrated, and one dilute. Add a small piece of Mg to each solution, and have the students explain why the results are so different. (I generally save this demonstration for kinetics at the beginning of Chapter 9.)

Development of the Topic

Show the listing of the percent alcohol on a wine label. Elicit other possible units of concentration. (Some possible answers include parts per million, proof, and scoops per cup.) Show the mathematical relationship between parts per million and percent by mass, and present a few problems using each.

Remind students of all the fun they had working with moles in the last chapter. They saw then that it is often most convenient to express quantities of chemicals in moles. Chemists often express the concentration of solutions in moles of solute per liter of solution. Define molarity, and present the equation

$$M = \frac{moles}{liter}$$

Present several problems, in increasing order of difficulty. Once you have established that your students can convert from molarity to moles and vice versa, provide a simple problem involving mass of solute, such as, "What is the molarity of a solution containing 80.0 grams of NaOH in 4.00 liters of solution?" Eventually work up to problems in which the solute is given in grams, and the volume in milliliters, emphasizing that such problems require three steps (grams to moles, milliliters to liters, moles divided by liters).

Show a bottle labeled "NaOH, 6 M." Pour out 100. mL and ask, "How much water would I need to add to dilute this solution to 3 molar?" Show students that molarity and volume vary inversely. Refer back to the other inverse relationship you have presented, between pressure and volume. Show that just as $P_1V_1 = P_2V_2$ in gas problems, $M_1V_1 = M_2V_2$ in dilution problems. In the problem given,

$$6\ M\ \text{NaOH} \times 100\ \text{mL} = 3\ M\ \text{NaOH} \times x\ \text{mL};\ x = 200\ \text{mL}$$

Emphasize that 200 mL is the desired final volume. To get this volume we need to add 100 mL of water to the 100 mL of NaOH solution we already have.

Teachers wishing to teach molality should present the definition and problems similar to those shown for molarity, culminating in, for example: What is the molality of a solution containing 20.0 grams of NaOH in 200. grams of water?

Topic IV *Properties of Solutions—Colligative Properties*

Goal: What properties of the solvent are changed by the presence of solute particles?

Instructional Objectives

Students will be able to:
1. Define an electrolyte as a substance that conducts electricity in solution.
2. Explain the conductivity of electrolytes in terms of mobile ions.
3. Describe the effect of a solute on the boiling point, freezing point, and vapor pressure of the solvent.
4. Predict how the dissociation of an electrolyte in water will affect the freezing point and boiling point of the solution.
5. Calculate the freezing point and boiling point of solutions given the concentration and depression or elevation constants of the solvent. (Allow an extra day if you wish to illustrate these problems.)

Motivation for the Topic

Teachers who do not mind a particularly grisly motivation might ask if any students have seen the movie *The Green Mile*. Before the authorities electrocute a convict, they dip a sponge in salt water, which they then apply to the convict's head. Why do they do this? Use a conductivity apparatus to illustrate that pure water does not conduct, but salt water does. Conductivity is one of the properties of a solvent that change when a solute is added.

Development of the Topic

Distinguish between electrolytes and nonelectrolytes in terms of the formation of mobile ions. Ask students why we put salt on the roads and sidewalks after a snowstorm. Use a thermometer in an ice-salt mixture to demonstrate that the freezing point is lowered by the presence of the solute. Some students might have an ice-cream-making machine that uses a mixture of salt and ice as the coolant. What purpose does the salt serve?

Point out that the freezing point of a solvent is decreased by the presence of any solute. The amount of freezing-point depression depends on the concentration of solute particles. Other properties that similarly depend on solute concentration include vapor pressure and boiling point. The greater the concentration of solute, the lower the freezing point, the lower the vapor pressure, and the greater the boiling point.

If you have taught the phase diagram in Chapter 1, you may now explain the changes in freezing and boiling point in terms of vapor pressure. (See text page 315.) You may wish to insert a thermometer into some boiling salt water to demonstrate boiling-point elevation, but if you do, be sure to use a saturated solution, so that you get a noticeable change!

Present the following information, and challenge the students to explain. When solutions of glucose ($C_6H_{12}O_6$), ethanol (C_2H_5OH), and sucrose ($C_{12}H_{22}O_{11}$) (give the formulas) are prepared in equal concentration, the solutions have the same freezing point. When solutions of glucose ($C_6H_{12}O_6$), sodium chloride (NaCl), and calcium chloride ($CaCl_2$) are prepared in equal concentration, the freezing point of the NaCl solution will go down twice as much as that of the glucose, and the freezing point of the $CaCl_2$ solution will go down three times as much as that of the glucose.

First establish that the freezing points of the nonelectrolyte solutions were the same. Then, have the students try to explain why NaCl and $CaCl_2$ were different from each other. Once they have arrived at the conclusion that the change in freezing point depends on the total concentration of particles, and that each ion must be treated as a separate particle, ask them to compare the freezing point of an Na_2SO_4 solution with that of $CaCl_2$ solution. Once you tell them that both are the same, challenge them to explain why. Conclude that the greater the total concentration of ions, the lower the freezing point and the higher the boiling point of the solution.

Teachers wishing to present problems using the molal freezing- and boiling-point constants can develop the concept by pointing out that since the change in these properties depends only on the particle concentration, there should be a way to calculate the change based on concentration. The concentration unit that is generally used in such calculations is molality. Present the equations, and try the sample problems given on pages 310–313. As an extra credit problem, with a really talented class, you may wish to try this. When 10.0 grams of a certain nonelectrolyte are dissolved in 100. grams of water, the solution freezes at −1.033°C. Given the freezing point depression constant of water, 1.86°/m, what is the molar mass of the nonelectrolyte? (180 g)

Suggested Laboratory Activities

1. **Construction of Solubility Curve**

   Using four test tubes, have students prepare 4-, 5-, 6-, and 7-gram samples of ammonium chloride in 10. grams of water. The test tubes are heated in a hot water bath until all of the solute dissolves. A thermometer is inserted in each tube and they are allowed to cool. The temperature is read at the first appearance of crystals. A solubility curve is constructed, and students are asked, on the basis of their experiment, to predict the solubility of ammonium chloride in 100 grams of water at 60°C.

2. **Conductivity of Aqueous Solutions**

   Schools that have an adequate supply of conductivity apparatuses can have students test a wide variety of solutes and draw conclusions based on their observations. I usually include calcium carbonate chips as one of the "solutes." Because it is ionic, students usually expect that it will be a strong electrolyte. I want them to see that an ionic substance is an electrolyte only if it is soluble!

Rates of Reactions: Kinetics

INTRODUCTION

The material in Chapters 9 through 11—kinetics, equilibrium, and thermodynamics—is often taught as a single unit. In previous editions of this text, thermodynamics was placed first. However, the three topics can be approached in almost any order. Most teachers will spend two to three weeks on the three chapters.

The emphasis in Chapter 9 is on factors that influence reaction rate and the interpretation of potential energy diagrams. Concepts such as rate law and rate order are omitted; a proper presentation would assume a level of mathematical sophistication possessed by very few high school sophomores.

Day	Lesson for the Day	Text Pages	Homework.
1–2	Factors that determine rate	321 to 332	Pg. 326, Practice 9.1–9.3; Pgs. 332–333, Practice 9.4; Pgs. 335–336, Chapter Review 1–8; Pg. 339, Constructed Response 2
3–4	Potential energy diagrams	333 to 334	Pg. 335, Practice 9.5–9.9; Pgs. 335–339, Chapter Review 9–26; Pg. 339, Constructed Response 1

Topic I Factors That Determine Rate (2 days)

Goal: How do we explain and predict rates of reaction?

Instructional Objectives

Students will be able to:
1. Predict the effect on reaction rate of changes in pressure, temperature, concentration, and surface area of solids.
2. Explain reaction rate in terms of collision theory.

Motivation for the Topic

A most dramatic motivating demonstration is the iodine clock. By varying the concentration and/or temperature, you can produce the sudden dramatic color change in a predetermined time interval. I like to pour the chemicals together, wait the appropriate amount of time, then point and say, "Presto change-o." Very impressive, when it works. I then elicit opinions on how I worked my miracle. We try it again, and the time is much slower. Why? (I dilute the mixture with a small amount of water.)

An alternative requiring far less time and preparation is to take two effervescent antacids, one in tablet form, another in powdered form, and simultaneously drop them in beakers of water. (I joke about needing fast, fast relief.)

Development of the Topic

The factors that control reaction rate can be elicited in an interesting way through a series of demonstrations. In addition to the antacid demonstration above, a small amount of lycopodium powder can be placed on a scupula, and carefully inserted into a flame. It will catch fire, and burn slowly. However, if the powder is quickly thrown through the flame, it will burn in one dramatic instant, often terrifying the students in the first row. **(Be sure to take appropriate, adequate safety precautions.)**

Two different concentrations of HCl reacted with magnesium will demonstrate the effect of concentration on reaction rate. The effect of temperature on reaction rate is demonstrated by dropping an effervescent antacid tablet into hot water. (Better, I think, not to tell the students in advance that it is hot water, and let them deduce it.)

A 4 percent solution of H_2O_2 can be used to demonstrate the effect of a catalyst, in this case manganese dioxide (MnO_2). Point out that the MnO_2 is still there after the reaction is complete. Since the reaction generates oxygen, you can relight a glowing splint in the oxygen, and ask why the splint burns better in oxygen than it does in air. To explain how a catalyst works, introduce the concepts of activation energy and activated complex. A catalyst often provides an alternate path from reactant to product. If the activated complex formed in the alternate path has lower energy than in the original path, then the activation energy is decreased. The lower the activation energy, the faster the reaction is.

Once you have established the variables that affect reaction rate (temperature, concentration, and surface area of solids), you can discuss the reasons each has an effect. Each must increase the number of effective collisions between the reacting particles. This can be done either by increasing collision frequently, or by increasing collision efficiency. Concentration and surface area affect collision frequency, catalysts affect collision efficiency, and temperature affects both.

Topic II Potential Energy Diagrams (2 days)

Goal: How are the energy changes that occur during chemical reactions shown graphically?

Instructional Objectives

Students will be able to:
1. On a given potential energy diagram, identify the heat of reaction, activation energy, and the potential energy of reactant and product.
2. Predict how the addition of a catalyst would change the potential energy diagram.
3. State the differences between endothermic and exothermic reactions in terms of the sign of ΔH, the change in potential energy, and the relative potential energy of the product and the reactant.

Motivation for the Topic

How do we cook hot dogs outdoors? Establish that the source of heat is the burning of charcoal, $C + O_2 \rightarrow CO_2$. This is an exothermic reaction. Where does the energy come from? Some of the potential energy stored by the reactants is converted to kinetic energy. The law of conservation of energy says that the amount of kinetic energy that is produced must be equal to the loss of potential energy. Let's take a look at what happens during this reaction in terms of potential energy.

Development of the Topic

Draw the coordinates of a graph with potential energy as the y-axis and reaction coordinate as the x-axis. Explain that the reaction coordinate shows the changes in the system over time. Show or elicit that the $C + O_2$ has a greater potential energy than that of the CO_2. All exothermic reactions involve a decrease in potential energy. Begin your potential energy diagram as shown below.

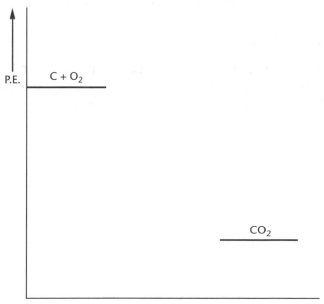

Then take out a few coals. "I have charcoal, the air has plenty of oxygen, so why isn't any heat being produced?" Students know that you need something to start the reaction. Explain that the energy needed to initiate the reaction is called activation energy. Since the activation energy is absorbed by the system, it increases the potential energy. Draw in the remainder of the potential energy curve and indicate, with an arrow, the activation energy.

Similarly develop on your diagram the arrow indicating ΔH, and the activation energy of the reverse reaction. Elicit that the reverse reaction would be endothermic, and that its ΔH would be equal in value, but opposite in sign.

Draw the arrow from the bottom of the diagram to the reactant (arrow 1 in Figure 9-8 in text), indicating that it represents the potential energy of the reactant. The potential energy of the reactant is "how high it is above the ground," the ground being the x-axis. Draw in the lines indicating the potential energy of the product, and of the activated complex.

Repeat the process of drawing a potential energy diagram, but this time show an endothermic reaction. Have students construct the curve, and draw in the six lines. Then ask what effect a catalyst would have on the system, and on the two diagrams. Use a dotted line, or colored chalk, to indicate the effect of a catalyst on the potential energy diagram.

Suggested Laboratory Activities

1. **Catalyzed Decomposition of Bleach**

   Ordinary household chlorine bleach is used. The production of oxygen from the bleach is catalyzed by cobalt nitrate [$Co(NO_3)_2$] solution. By collecting the oxygen in graduated cylinders, students can plot the rate of reaction at varying concentrations of bleach and at varying temperatures.

2. **Iodine Clock**

   This requires much more careful preparation than for the first suggestion, but is more impressive. Students find the time needed for the dramatic change in color, and study the effect of varying the concentration of iodate ion.

10 Equilibrium

INTRODUCTION

While much of the quantitative material will be found in the "Taking a Closer Look" section, the discussion of the equilibrium constant is in the main body of the chapter. Understanding the significance of the equilibrium constant enables students to gain a deeper appreciation of Le Chatelier's Principle. Similarly, although it is possible to illustrate the common ion effect without referring to the K_{SP}, many will think it preferable to include K_{SP}, as we have done.

In the sample lessons that follow, Le Chatelier's Principle is presented after developing the effects of the various stresses on equilibrium systems. You may prefer to develop the material *from* Le Chatelier's Principle; both methods have merit.

The chapter contains a section on reactions that go to completion. This includes showing how a table of solubilities can be used to predict precipitation, and a discussion of the net ionic equation in a precipitation reaction.

Day	Lesson for the Day	Text Pages	Homework
1	How systems reach equilibrium	341 to 347	Pg. 347, Practice 10.2; Pg. 374, Chapter Review 4, 7
2	How concentration affects equilibrium	347 to 352	Pg. 351, Practice 10.4
3–4	How pressure and temperature changes affect equilibrium	352 to 362	Pg. 354, Practice 10.5; Pg. 358, Practice 10.7, 10.8; Pg. 362, Practice 10.9, 10.10
5	Solutions and equilibrium	362 to 364	Pg. 364, Practice 10.11–10.13
6	Precipitation reactions	365 to 367	Pgs. 367–368, Practice 10.14–10.17

Topic I How Systems Reach Equilibrium (2 days)?

Goal: How do systems reach equilibrium?

Instructional Objectives

Students will be able to:
1. Describe equilibrium as a condition of constant concentration.
2. Describe equilibria in terms of the rates of forward and reverse reactions.
3. Recognize that equilibrium does not imply equal concentrations of product and reactant.
4. Chart how a reaction reaches equilibrium by showing the changes in the rates of the forward and reverse reactions.
5. Predict the effect of changes in concentration on equilibrium systems.
6. Write the equilibrium expression given a balanced chemical equation.
7. State the significance of the numerical value of the equilibrium constant.

Motivation for the Topic

An abandoned tennis court surrounded by a high fence is visited by two young men, Joe and Schmoe. On the court are 100 old tennis balls, randomly distributed. The two boys get on opposite sides of the court and decide to play a game. The idea is to get all the tennis balls to the other player's side of the court. Both players start throwing the balls as quickly as they can to the other side of the court. What happens? (Students generally guess that no one wins, or that 50 tennis balls end up at on each side.) I then add, "I should have told you that Joe is a very good athlete, while Schmoe has bursitis and gout. What happens?" Eventually, we conclude that more of the tennis balls end up on Schmoe's side, but as Joe starts running out of tennis balls, it takes him longer to throw them back. As Schmoe accumulates tennis balls, he can get to the next one faster. Eventually, their rates become equal. (See Figure 10-1 in the text, which I label "Joe's Rate" and "Schmoe's Rate" instead of "Forward" and "Backward.") Chemical reactions reach equilibrium in very much the same way as Joe and Schmoe.

Development of the Topic

Suppose at equilibrium there are 80 tennis balls on Schmoe's side, to 20 on Joe's side. How do we know that the system is at equilibrium? First, the number of balls on each side is constant. Second, the rates are the same in both directions. However, the number of balls on each side is not the same.

How would the situation change if we moved the fence in on Schmoe's side of the court, making his court smaller? Schmoe would be able to get to the balls faster. Equilibrium depends not on the number of balls, but on the concentration of balls. In this case, equilibrium is reached when the concentration on Schmoe's side is four times the concentration on Joe's side. Suppose we threw five more tennis balls over the fence. What do we expect would happen? Equilibrium would be reached at 21 and 84, maintaining the same ratio of four to one. In chemical reactions also, equilibrium is reached at a definite ratio of product concentration to reactant concentration. This ratio is called the equilibrium constant.

What would happen if there was a hole in the fence? Students will correctly conclude that balls would occasionally leave the court, and the system would never reach equilibrium. Equilibrium is reached only in a closed system.

Summarize by applying the concept of equilibrium to phase equilibrium (a closed bottle of water), solution equilibrium (a saturated solution), and chemical equilibrium (as in the reaction $2 NO_2 \rightleftarrows N_2O_4$). You can use NO_2 tubes to demonstrate the equilibrium—a constant color is reached at a given temperature.

The effect of changes in concentration on equilibrium systems can be discussed either qualitatively or quantitatively, depending upon whether the teacher wishes to use equilibrium expressions and the K_{EQ}. We have already established that how fast the boys can throw tennis balls depends on the concentration of tennis balls. What should happen if we increase the concentration of a substance that appears on one side of a chemical equation? There are several reactions that can be used to illustrate the concept. For example,

$$SbCl_3 + 3 H_2O \rightleftarrows Sb(OH)_3 + 3 HCl$$

(or, if you prefer, $Sb^{3+} + 3 H_2O \rightleftarrows Sb(OH)_3 + 3 H^+$)

Begin with an acidic solution of $SbCl_3$, and add water. A milky precipitate forms. What can we add that will drive the reaction backward? Add HCl and the precipitate disappears. Then add more H_2O, and the precipitate reappears. Increasing the concentration of reactant drives the reaction forward; increasing the concentration of product drives the reaction backward.

Show an orange solution of sodium dichromate ($Na_2Cr_2O_7$). Add NaOH; the solution will turn yellow. The reaction is

$$Cr_2O_7{}^{2-} + 2 OH^- \rightleftarrows 2CrO_4{}^{2-} + H_2O$$

Point out that the addition of acid will remove OH^- ions. What effect will the removal of these ions have on the system? Demonstrate that adding nitric or sulfuric acid turns the solution orange. Removing a reactant drives a reaction toward the reactant side. What would removing a product do?

Summarize with a reaction like this one: $NO + SO_3 \rightleftarrows NO_2 + SO_2$. What three different steps could you take to increase the concentration of SO_2 at equilibrium?

Teachers wishing to include a more quantitative approach should emphasize that a change in concentration does not change the value of the K_{EQ}. When additional NO is added, for example, the reaction must produce more product in order to get back to the same value of K_{EQ}.

Topic II Le Chatelier's Principle (2 days)

Goal: How can we drive an equilibrium system in a desired direction?

Instructional Objectives

Students will be able to:
1. Predict the effect of changes in pressure and volume on equilibrium systems.
2. Predict the effect of changes in temperature on equilibrium systems.
3. Recognize whether a reaction is endothermic or exothermic when "heat" is written into the chemical equation.
4. Provide an optimum set of conditions, in terms of pressure and temperature, to drive a given reaction in a given direction.

Motivation for the Topic

$$N_2 \ (g) + 3 \ H_2 \ (g) \rightleftarrows 2 \ NH_3 \ (g)$$

Ammonia is a very important industrial chemical. It can be oxidized to produce nitrates, which are used to improve crop yields. Until 1911, though, chemists were unable to use the reaction above to produce significant amounts of ammonia. This was a serious problem for Germany, because nitrates are also needed to make gunpowder. The great German chemist Fritz Haber solved the problem of how to make this reaction produce the maximum quantity of product. How can we shift a reaction in a desired direction?

Development of the Topic

We have already discussed how we can drive a reaction by changing the concentration of its components. (Students should be able to tell you that this reaction can be shifted forward by increasing the concentrations of nitrogen and hydrogen, and by decreasing the concentration of ammonia in the system.)

What other factor might be significant in reactions involving gases? (If students answer "temperature," assure them that they are correct, but temperature change affects all systems, not just those containing gases.)

How would our system be affected by a change in pressure? The rule is that an increase in pressure drives the reaction in the direction that produces fewer moles of gas. In the ammonia synthesis, the reactant contains 4 moles of gas to every 2 moles of product. Therefore an increase in pressure will drive the reaction forward, producing more ammonia. How can we increase the pressure in a system without adding more material, and without changing the temperature? A decrease in volume increases the pressure, and drives the reaction to the side with the smaller volume, i.e., the side with fewer moles of gas. Haber performed the reaction at very high pressures.

$$CaCO_3 \ (s) \rightleftarrows CaO \ (s) + CO_2 \ (g)$$

What effect would decreasing the volume of the system have on this reaction? The product contains 1 mole of gas, but there are no gases in the reactant. A decrease in volume will drive this reaction backward, producing more $CaCO_3$ and less CaO.

An explanation of why reactions shift in response to pressure changes requires use of the K_{EQ} and the equilibrium expression. A change in pressure does not change the value of the K_{EQ}. Suppose we halved the volume in our ammonia reaction. All of the concentrations (and all of the pressures) would double. The equilibrium expression is

$$\frac{[NH_3]^2}{[N_2][H_2]^3}$$

In this case, when the concentrations all double, the numerator becomes four times larger, but the denominator becomes sixteen times larger. The fraction has decreased in value. To get back to the K_{EQ}, some reactant must turn into product.

Students generally do suggest that a change in temperature ought to affect an equilibrium system. But how? NO_2 tubes offer an apt and attractive demonstration of the effect of temperature on equilibrium. Give the reaction

$$2 \ NO_2 \ (g) \rightleftarrows N_2O_4 \ (g) + heat$$

Show two tubes, and point out that NO_2 is dark brown, while N_2O_4 is colorless. We can therefore see the direction of any shifts in the system by observing changes in color. What do you predict will happen when a gas tube is heated? Immerse a tube in very hot water. The color of the heated tube darkens. What does this indicate? The reaction shifted away from the heat. Reactions in which heat is a product are exothermic. (How else can we indicate that a reaction is exothermic?) An increase in temperature drives a reaction in the endothermic direction. What happens when we decrease the temperature?

For the reaction $N_2 \ (g) + 3 \ H_2 \ (g) \rightleftarrows 2 \ NH_3 \ (g)$, ΔH is -92 kJ. What must be done in terms of temperature to drive this reaction forward? The reaction shifts to the right when the temperature is decreased. Yet, Haber had to perform the reaction at relatively high temperatures (over 400°C). Why? Remind students of the effect of temperature on the rate of reaction.

To summarize, I present a test tube of $CoCl_2$ dissolved in ethanol. The color is intensely blue. The reaction, when water is added is,

$$CoCl_2 + 6\ H_2O \rightleftarrows Co(H_2O)_6^{2+} + 2\ Cl^- + heat$$

Add just a few drops of water. The solution turns pink. Prepare several solutions with the same initial color. The color becomes bluer when the solution is heated, or when a few drops of concentrated HCl are added. It becomes pinker when additional water is added.

AgCl is insoluble, so if we add some silver ions to the solution, it will remove chloride ions. What effect will that have on the color of the solution? (The resulting solution greatly resembles a popular remedy for upset stomach!)

Teachers who have chosen to include consideration of the role of the equilibrium constant in these processes should point out that a change in temperature does change the value of K_{EQ}, and compare the effect of increasing temperature on exothermic vs. endothermic reactions.

We have learned the effects of changes in temperature, pressure, and concentration on equilibrium systems. All three of these are summarized in one famous statement, Le Chatelier's Principle. I end the discussion by showing how Le Chatelier's Principle applies to each of the three variables. (Many of my colleagues prefer to present Le Chatelier's Principle first, and then have students predict the effects of the three variables based on Le Chatelier.)

Topic III Solutions and Equilibrium (1–2 days)

Goal: How are equilibrium concepts applied to saturated solutions?

Instructional Objectives

Students will be able to:
*1. Describe K_{SP} as an equilibrium constant used in predicting the behavior of ionic substances in water.
*2. Write the correct expression for the K_{SP}, given the formula of a salt.
*3. Predict the relative solubility of a salt based on the value of the K_{SP}.
4. Explain the effect of a common ion on the solubility of a given salt.
5. Predict the direction of a solubility equation based on Le Chatelier's Principle.
6. Predict the solubility of salts based on a solubility table.
7. Write the net equation for a precipitation reaction.

*Teachers who have chosen to leave out the discussion of the equilibrium constant will omit these objectives, and are likely to spend one day on this material, rather than two.

Motivation for the Topic

React solutions of lead(II) nitrate ($Pb(NO_3)_2$) and sodium iodide (NaI) in a large test tube. Elicit that a precipitate is an insoluble product. What is the insoluble product in this reaction? How can we tell?

Development of the Topic

(Teachers wishing to omit the discussion of K_{SP} should skip ahead to the third paragraph in this development.)

The precipitate is PbI_2. We can write an equation for what might happen when PbI_2 is placed in water: PbI_2 (s) → Pb_2+ (aq) + 2 I^- (aq). Show, that because solids are omitted from equilibrium expressions, $K = [Pb^{2+}][I^-]^2$. This equilibrium constant is called the K_{SP}, or solubility product constant. These constants are listed in chemist's reference tables. The K_{SP} of PbI_2 is 1.4×10^{-8}. Establish that precipitation occurs when salts form that have a low K_{SP}. What is the relationship between K_{SP} and solubility? Point out that since the K_{SP} is not zero, the salt is not completely insoluble. The term "insoluble" is generally applied to substances with very low solubility.

What effect would an increase in temperature have on the value of the K_{SP}? Why? (Students should be able to relate the effect of temperature on the K_{SP} to the fact that the dissolving of a salt is generally an endothermic process.)

What would happen if we added some NaI to a saturated solution of PbI_2? Use Le Chatelier's Principle to show that the addition of I^- drives the equilibrium toward the formation of PbI_2 (s). What happens to the Pb^{2+} ion concentration when additional I^- ions are added to the solution?

We learned in our discussion of solubility that water is often a good solvent for ionic substances. We see, however, that not all such substances are soluble. To predict a precipitation reaction, we need to know which of our possible products are soluble, and which are not. Tables such as this one (show or distribute a table like the "Solubility Guidelines" on page 592, in Appendix 4 of the text) enable us to predict the solubility of many different salts.

How can we use this table to predict the solubility of the salts produced in our reaction?

$$Pb(NO_3)_2 + 2\ NaI → PbI_2 + 2\ NaNO_3$$

(Students should be able to predict the products.)

Students should notice that according to the guidelines, halides are soluble except when combined with Ag^+, Pb^{2+}, and Hg_2^{2+}. Therefore PbI_2 should be insoluble. Group 1 ions, such as Na^+, always form soluble compounds. Therefore $NaNO_3$ should be soluble.

Show how, since the sodium and nitrate ions remain in the solution throughout the reaction, the net reaction is Pb^{2+} (aq) + 2 I^- (aq) → PbI_2 (s). The sodium and nitrate ions are *spectator* ions.

Have students predict what will happen when you mix $BaCl_2$ solution with Na_2CrO_4. Perform the reaction, and have your students write the net chemical equation. Repeat with several other reactions, such as barium chloride with magnesium sulfate, barium hydroxide with iron(II) sulfate (forms 2 precipitates), copper sulfate with potassium carbonate. Ask students to predict what will happen when copper sulfate solution is added to a solution of magnesium chloride. Demonstrate that no precipitate forms, as the students should have predicted.

Suggested Laboratory Activity

A Qualitative Analysis Based on the Solubility Guidelines

Students are told in advance that they will be given five bottles, labeled A, B, C, D, and E, that will contain solutions of $BaCl_2$, $CuCl_2$, $CuSO_4$, $NaNO_3$, and KOH. Their task is, by reacting these chemicals with one another, to determine which solution is in which bottle. They must design their own procedure, but before performing the experiment, they must fill in a grid, using "P" for "precipitate, or "N" for "no precipitate," based on the solubility guidelines. They are also reminded that two of the solutions are colored; they should be able to figure out which two.

Sample grid:

	$CuSO_4$	$BaCl_2$	$CuCl_2$	$NaNO_3$	KOH
$CuSO_4$		P	N	N	P
$BaCl_2$	P		N	N	N
$CuCl_2$	N	N		N	P
$NaNO_3$	N	N	N		N
KOH	P	N	P	N	

In the lab, the students are given a test tube rack with several test tubes, and the five solutions, preferably in dropper-bottles. The more test tubes provided, the better the results are likely to be, since the only likely errors are due to inadequately rinsing the test tubes between uses.

Students' logic may run something like this:
- The one that never forms a precipitate is the $NaNO_3$.
- The colored solution that forms only one precipitate is $CuCl_2$.
- The solution that reacts with $CuCl_2$ is KOH.
- The colorless solution that forms only one precipitate is $BaCl_2$. It precipitates only with $CuSO_4$.

11

The Forces That Drive Reactions

INTRODUCTION

In this chapter we deal with basic thermodynamics, presenting the state functions, ΔH, ΔG, and ΔS. The relationships among these functions and their significance in driving chemical reactions are discussed qualitatively and quantitatively. The use of free energy and enthalpy of formation is discussed in the "Taking a Closer Look" section of the chapter.

Day	Lesson for the Day	Text Pages	Homework
1–2	Enthalpy (ΔH)	382 to 388	Pgs. 388–389, Practice 11.1–11.4
3	Entropy (ΔS)	389 to 393	Pg. 392, Practice 11.5; Pg. 393, Practice 11.6, 11.7
4	Spontaneous reactions	393 to 395	Pg. 396, Practice 11.9 a
5	Free energy change	395 to 396	Pg. 396, Practice 11.9 b, 11.10

Topic I *Enthalpy Change (2 days)*

Goal: How is enthalpy change used in predicting the results of physical and chemical changes?

Instructional Objectives

Students will be able to:
1. Describe an exothermic change as one in which potential energy is converted to kinetic energy, and the sign of ΔH is negative, and similarly correctly describe an endothermic change.
2. Using a table of ΔH values, find the enthalpy change for a given quantity of reactant or product.
3. State that reactions tend to go in the direction of decreased enthalpy—the exothermic direction.
4. Interpret thermochemical equations.

Motivation for the Topic

How is your home heated in the winter? If students say they have gas heat, ask them how it works. Establish that the gas is methane (CH_4), and it is burned to produce heat, which is then generally used to boil water, sending steam into the radiators. Why do we use that particular gas? Aside from cost and safety, a small amount of CH_4 can produce a large amount of heat. The heat produced is called the heat of reaction, or the enthalpy change, ΔH.

Development of the Topic

Students should already know that ΔH is negative for any exothermic reaction. Write the equation for the combustion of methane

$$CH_4 + 2\,O_2 \rightarrow CO_2 + 2\,H_2O$$

and write $\Delta H = -890.4$ kilojoules. Elicit from the students the meaning of the value of ΔH. Emphasize that the 890.4 kJ is the amount of heat released when the number of moles shown in the balanced equation react. How much heat is produced when 0.500 mole of CH_4 (g) burns to produce CO_2 (g) and H_2O (l)? If you wish, you can illustrate a problem in which the quantity of methane is given in grams instead of moles; it serves as a useful review of previously taught material.

What gas is used in outdoor barbecues? Provide a table showing the heat of reaction of several compounds, as in Table I in Appendix 4. Point out that propane is C_3H_8, and have a student tell you that it produces 2219.2 kilojoules per mole. What other substances in the list produce large amounts of heat when they combine with oxygen? Students will tell you that octane, which is burned in car engines, and glucose produce large amounts of energy. Where is glucose burned? Students seldom come up with the answer—in living cells.

Should you wish to demonstrate the meaning of the large values of ΔH in a dramatic fashion, mix roughly equal amounts of ordinary table sugar (powdered, or confectioners', sugar works even better) and potassium chlorate in a small beaker. Using a long glass medicine dropper, or a long glass tube, carefully add three or four drops of concentrated sulfuric acid. Step back immediately! (Try this out in the lab before using it in class.) **(Be sure to take appropriate and adequate safety precautions.)** The rapid combustion of the sugar is extremely impressive, with the flame shooting several inches into the air. Because the reaction produces a cloud of sugar dust, it is best done at the end of the day, right before the class leaves the room.

You may also show the class an alcohol lamp; the combustion reaction of ethanol is included in the reference table cited above. Write the reaction for the combustion of ethanol as follows:

$$C_2H_5OH \ (l) + 3 \ O_2 \ (g) \rightarrow 2 \ CO_2 \ (g) + 3 \ H_2O \ (l) + 1367 \ kJ$$

Explain that when written in this form, we call the equation a thermochemical equation. It includes the heat in the balanced equation. But ΔH is negative. Why is there a plus sign (+) in front of the 1367 kJ? In this case, the plus sign means "and." The reaction produces carbon dioxide, water, and heat. In an exothermic reaction, the heat appears in the product. What is ΔH in the following reaction?

$$C_2H_2 \ (g) + H_2 \ (g) \rightarrow C_2H_4 \ (g) + 175 \ kJ$$

Make sure that your students answer "$\Delta H = -175$ kJ." How much heat is produced in the reaction? (175 kJ per mole) Students often wonder why the minus sign is not used in the second question. I say to them, "Let's say that I go to Atlantic City, and lose 100 dollars. If my wife asks me how I did, I will answer '–100 dollars.' But if she asks me, 'How much did you lose this time?' I answer, '100 dollars.' Since she has already specified that the money was lost, I don't need to include the minus sign. When you write the heat in the product, you are already stating that it was produced; the minus sign is superfluous."

Remind students that in an exothermic reaction, the potential energy decreases. The amount of heat produced is equal to the change in potential energy. Exothermic reactions convert potential energy to kinetic energy. Discuss the relationship between potential energy and stability. Reactions tend to produce products that are more stable. Potential energy tends to decrease in chemical change much the same way that in a room, the most likely place to find a ball is on the floor.

Topic II *Spontaneous Change (2–3 days)*

Goal: What determines whether a chemical or physical change occurs spontaneously?

Instructional Objectives

Students will be able to:
1. Define entropy as a measure of the randomness of a system.
2. Compare the entropy of substances when given their states.
3. Predict whether a given chemical reaction or physical change will lead to increased or decreased entropy.

4. State that decreased potential energy and increased entropy favor spontaneous reactions, or that the best combination for a spontaneous reaction is an exothermic reaction that produces an increase in randomness.

5. Describe ΔG as the free energy, and use the sign of ΔG to predict the spontaneity of reactions.

Motivation for the Topic

Take out a new deck of cards. Unwrap it, and ask if anyone wants to play poker with you. What must you do before you play? Why? If no students know this, point out that in a new deck, the cards are arranged from ace to king in every suit. Why do you shuffle cards? Elicit that you shuffle to make the arrangement of the cards random. With each shuffle, does the deck become more random, or less random? In nature, as in shuffling, systems tend to become more random.

Development of the Topic

Draw the system shown on text page 390, and let students predict what will happen when the barrier between the gases is removed. The drive to increased randomness is just as important as the drive to decreased potential energy. Scientists give the name "entropy" to the randomness of a system. While entropy is measurable, we will concern ourselves for now only with relative entropy. Ask students to predict the relative entropy of ice, water, and steam, and to explain their choices. Summarize that as we go from solid to liquid to gas, both the entropy and the potential energy increase.

In nature the entropy tends to increase. (When your parent tells you to clean up your room, tell him or her that your chemistry teacher says, "You can't fight entropy!") But potential energy tends to decrease. That means that entropy favors steam, while energy favors ice. For a spontaneous change to occur, at least one of the two factors must be favorable. Ice can melt, when it is warm enough, because the entropy increases when ice melts. Water can freeze, when it is cold enough, because the potential energy decreases during freezing, an exothermic process. Changes in which both factors are favorable, that lead to increased randomness and decreased potential energy, are spontaneous at *any* temperature. (You may wish to copy the table at the top of page 395.)

Dissolve a large amount of ammonium nitrate (NH_4NO_3) in a beaker of water and stir. Have a student observe that the solution becomes very cold. What type of change is this? Point out that the bonds within the ionic solid are stronger than the bonds between the ions and the water.

$$NH_4NO_3 \ (s) + 25.69 \ kJ \rightarrow NH_4^+ \ (aq) + NO_3^- \ (aq)$$

Why is the heat written on the reactant side? This reaction is endothermic. It produces an increase in potential energy. Why does it occur at all? Elicit that the dissolving process increased the entropy of the system.

Summarize by performing the reaction between barium hydroxide and ammonium thiocyanate.

$$Ba(OH)_2 \bullet 8\ H_2O\ (s) + 2\ NH_4SCN\ (s) \rightarrow 10\ H_2O\ (l) + Ba(SCN)_2\ (aq) + 2\ NH_3\ (g)$$

(Barium hydroxide is normally sold as a hydrate.)

Mix the two solids in a small beaker, and have a student stir the mixture. You might try resting the beaker on a small, wet piece of wood. As the mixture is stirred, it liquefies, and becomes so cold that the wood freezes to the bottom of the beaker. The odor of ammonia gas becomes apparent as well. **(Be sure there is adequate ventilation, or use a fume hood.)** Elicit that this is an endothermic reaction. In order for it to occur spontaneously, what must be happening to the entropy? What observations lead us to conclude that the entropy is increasing? (The mixture started out solid, and produced a liquid and a gas.)

You might also ask your students why the water beneath the beaker froze, while the water within the beaker did not. Do they still remember that a solute produces a freezing-point depression? (Freezing-point depression is something that happens when you are sick and tired of winter weather!)

To motivate a discussion of ΔG, remind students that when, as in the case of ice melting, one of the two factors, (ΔH and ΔS) is favorable, the reaction will happen under some conditions, and not others. To predict the course of such reactions, we have to combine the effects of ΔH, ΔS, and temperature. The result of considering all of these factors, ΔG, is found using the equation

$$\Delta G = \Delta H - T\Delta S$$

(Emphasize that the temperature must be Kelvin.) The sign of ΔG tells us whether the reaction is spontaneous under the given set of conditions. If ΔG is negative, the reaction is spontaneous. If ΔG is positive, the reaction is not spontaneous. If ΔG is positive, what can you predict about ΔG for the reverse reaction? If it is so cold in the room that ice will not melt, what can you conclude would happen to water in that room? What would it tell you if ΔG for a change was zero? Point out that for any system at equilibrium, ΔG must equal zero.

Suggested Laboratory Activity

Determination of the Heat of Solution of NH_4Cl or NH_4NO_3

The experiment requires the use of a Styrofoam cup, a thermometer, a balance, water, and the salt being tested. You can require the students to express their result in either joules per gram of salt or joules per mole.

Assume that the specific heat of the mixture is 4.2 J/g°. I recommend that you use about 100 grams of water and about 10 grams of the salt. The students will need to estimate the temperatures to the nearest tenth of a degree; otherwise, the result has only one significant figure. The actual values are 26.5 kJ/mol for the NH_4NO_3, and 16.3 kJ/mol for the NH_4Cl. The experimental values will come out about 10% lower than that, if the experiment is done well.

12 Acids and Bases

INTRODUCTION

As noted in the introduction to Chapter 10, I think that equilibrium constants should be presented in a basic first-year high school chemistry course. However, many teachers prefer to take a less quantitative approach. Therefore, the discussion of K_A, K_B is found in the "Taking a Closer Look" section of the chapter.

Since so many students are using calculators, the text includes a section on pH calculations using logarithms. Those teachers who wish to go only as far as "each pH unit represents a factor of ten" will find that they can easily skip from the middle of page 414 to the bottom of page 416.

More than in most topics, this one gives students the opportunity to really do some "wet" chemistry, and gives teachers a chance to perform several colorful and interesting demonstrations.

Day	Lesson for the Day	Text Pages	Homework
1–2	Defining acids and bases	406 to 410	Pg. 410, Practice 12.1; Pg. 436, Chapter Review 20; Pg. 438, Constructed Response 3
3	pH and indicators	410 to 414	Pg. 413, Practice 12.2–12.5; Pg. 414, Practice 12.6–12.9
4	pH calculations	414 to 416	Pg. 415, Practice 12.10, 12.11; Pg. 416, Practice 12.12, 12.13
5–6	Neutralization	416 to 422	Pgs. 421–422, Practice 12.14–12.16
7–8	Other acid-base theories	422 to 429	Pgs. 425–426, Practice 12.17–12.19; Pg. 429, Practice 12.20, 12.21

Topic I Definitions of Acids and Bases (2 days)

Goal: What are acids and bases?

Instructional Objectives

Students will be able to:
1. Define acids and bases operationally, in terms of their chemical behaviors.

65

2. State the Arrhenius definitions of acids and bases.
3. Identify and name several common acids and bases.

Motivation for the Topic

Add a piece of mossy zinc to a large test tube containing hydrochloric acid. (Use acid that is at least 3 molar.) Ask the class what is happening to the metal, and have them guess what the liquid in the test tube was. Students generally guess that the liquid was an acid.

Alternatively, if any of your students have tropical fish, ask them whether they test the pH of the water, and ask why they do so.

Establish that there is a class of compounds called acids that have certain common properties. What are the properties of acids?

Development of the Topic

Show a can of cola beverage and one of lemonade; have a student read the ingredients. What effect do acids have on the tastes of the beverages? [On several brands of lemonade, the list of ingredients contains the phrase "citric acid (provides tartness)"]. Establish that acids have a tart, or sour, taste. In many languages, the same word is used to mean both sour and acidic. (In German, for example, the word is "sauer.") Thousands of years ago, people observed that certain substances that tasted sour had other properties in common. Those substances are acids. What other properties do acids have in common?

Show that metals such as zinc, aluminum, and magnesium react with acids. (Again, using an HCl solution of at least 3 molar is recommended.) Use a burning splint to "pop" the hydrogen that is produced. Acids react with many metals to produce hydrogen.

Ask if students have ever heard the phrase "a litmus test." Show that litmus paper turns red in an acidic solution. Indicate that acids cause color changes in certain chemicals called indicators.

Students will also be able to tell you that acids have a low pH, although at this point they probably will not know what pH means.

Use a conductivity apparatus to show that pure water is a poor conductor of electricity. Elicit that solutions that contain mobile ions will conduct electricity. (This point was covered in the bonding unit, Chapter 3.) Point out that HCl is a molecular substance. Add some HCl to the water. Why does this solution conduct electricity? Show that several different acid solutions also conduct electricity. In fact, all acidic solutions conduct electricity.

Point out that Arrhenius explained why acids conduct electricity. He stated that electrolytes must form free ions in solution. Acids produce the H^+ ion in water. State the Arrhenius definition of acids. Show how the negative side of the polar water molecule can attract the H^+ ion, forming the hydronium ion, H_3O^+. Indicate that the H^+ and the H_3O^+ ion are used interchangeably to indicate acidity in aqueous solutions.

Use a similar procedure to illustrate the properties of bases, and to develop the Arrhenius definition of a base.

Topic II pH and Indicators (2 days)

Goal: How do we test the acidity and basicity of solutions?

Instructional Objectives

Students will be able to:
1. Compare the acidity and basicity of solutions based on their relative pH values.
2. Define a neutral solution as one with a pH of 7.
3. Use a table of indicators (e.g., Table M in Appendix 4) to predict the color of a given indicator based on the pH of a solution.
4. Identify which indicator might be best for a given purpose.
5. Find the pH of a solution given the H^+ or OH^- concentration.

Motivation for the Topic

Show the class a set of "color change" markers. (The ones I use are made by Crayola.) Demonstrate that the colors produced by the markers change when they are treated with the "color changer." How do these markers work? Show that the same color changes can be accomplished using a brush dipped in a dilute ammonia solution. Elicit that the dyes in the markers are actually acid-base indicators.

Using 500-mL beakers, prepare solutions of many different indicators, including methyl orange, Congo red, bromthymol blue, and phenolphthalein. Add a few drops of dilute NaOH to each, and stir. Then, add a few drops of dilute HCl, until the color changes, and stir again. Ask, "What is an indicator?"

Development of the Topic

The goal of the lesson is "How do we test the acidity or basicity of a solution?" One method is with indicators. Ask the class if they can think of another method. Remind them that they have already learned that pH can be used to indicate whether a solution is acidic or basic.

Define pH as a scale used to measure how acidic or basic a solution is. Point out that a change of one pH unit represents a *tenfold* change in the $[H^+]$. The lower the pH, the more acidic the solution, so a solution with a pH of 2 is 100 times more acidic than a solution with a pH of 4. Draw a number line on the board, showing how solutions go from strongly acidic, to weakly acidic, to neutral (at pH = 7), to weakly basic, to strongly basic, as the pH increases from 0 to 14. If time permits, you may want to use a pH meter to test several common substances. Students are generally surprised to discover that cola beverages have a pH of about 2.5.

If you wish to present a more quantitative treatment, define pH as $-\log$ [H$^+$]. Show how the concentration of H$^+$ ion can be used to find the precise pH. (See text pages 414 to 416.)

Add some methyl orange to a sample of pure water. It turns yellow, which is listed as the "base color" of that indicator. What is the indicator telling us about the pH of the solution? Each indicator has its own pH range. In solutions below these pH values, it shows its acid color, while above, it shows its base color.

Present a table listing indicators and their pH range, such as Table M in Appendix 4. Ask the class the following questions.

Why does methyl orange appear yellow in water? (The pH water is 7, which is in its base range.)

What color would phenolphthalein be in water? (Colorless)

What color would bromthymol blue be in water? (If the water is neutral, the solution will turn green.)

At pH 7, bromthymol blue is midway between its base range, where it is blue, and its acid range, where it is yellow. What happens when we mix blue and yellow? Have the students predict the colors of various indicators at various pH values. Soda water has a pH of about 4, while vinegar has a pH of about 3. Which indicator could be used to distinguish between these two solutions? (Bromcresol green)

Topic III *Neutralization (2 days)*

Goal: What happens when acids react with bases?

Instructional Objectives

Students will be able to:
1. Write the general chemical equation for neutralization of a strong acid with a strong base.
2. Write a balanced neutralization reaction for a given acid and base.
3. Describe the equipment and procedures used in an acid-base titration.
4. Solve problems using the titration equation $M \times V$ (H$^+$) $= M \times V$ (OH$^-$).
5. State that the reaction of an acid with a base produces a salt and water.

Motivation for the Topic

Ask whether your students are familiar with the medical condition known as heartburn. Point out that it is also called acid indigestion. What kind of drug do you take to relieve this condition? Take out a package of Rolaids or Mylanta (these brands use magnesium hydroxide, which serves our purpose better than other preparations using phosphates or calcium carbonate) and have a student note the active ingredient. Why would you take magnesium hydroxide to relieve acid indigestion?

Development of the Topic

Point out that stomach acid is HCl. What happens when HCl reacts with $Mg(OH)_2$? Write the equation on the board, and have a student balance it. Show that an acid is reacting with a base to produce a salt and water, and define this type of reaction as neutralization. (Students should also recall that this is a type of double replacement reaction.) Have students predict the products of other possible neutralizations, and have them suggest which acid and base should be used to produce a given salt.

Show bottles of NaOH and HCl and ask how these solutions could be used to produce a neutral product. Establish that you would have to add an equal number of moles of NaOH and HCl. Elicit that you could use an indicator or a pH meter to determine when the solution became neutral. Show that the NaOH is 0.4 molar, while the HCl is 0.2 molar. Add 20.0 mL of the HCl to an Erlenmeyer flask, and ask how many milliliters of the NaOH solution would be needed to produce a neutral solution. The process of mixing measured volumes of reagents until a desired end-point is reached is called *titration.* In this case, the objective is to titrate until the solution is neutral, or until the moles of H^+ = the moles of OH^-. Such an end-point is called the *equivalence point.* Add some phenolphthalein to the HCl solution, pointing out that one drop of extra base will turn the solution pink.

Show how a burette is used, and point out that burettes are used in titrations because they permit constant and precise monitoring of the volume of a solution as it is added to a reaction vessel. Titrate the HCl solution with the NaOH, illustrating that the end-point occurs when 10.0 mL of NaOH were added. Elicit that since the NaOH was twice as concentrated, it makes sense that you need an amount equal to half the volume of the HCl. At the equivalence point, the volumes were not equal, but the number of moles of acid and base *were* equal. Remind students that *molarity* × *volume = moles.* Therefore, at the equivalence point, $M \times V$ $(H^+) = M \times V$ (OH^-).

Show how a titration can be used to find the molarity of an acid or base of unknown concentration. Provide several titration problems using the equation above.

Topic IV *Other Acid-Base Theories (1–2 days)*

Note: Extensive discussion of Brønsted-Lowry theory would require at least two lessons. However, if one simply wishes to illustrate that there are alternate acid-base theories, without presenting them in detail, then half of one period is sufficient. While the text provides a detailed discussion, including the relative strengths of sets of acid-base pairs, the following lesson focuses on the definitions, which probably is sufficient in most high school chemistry programs.

Goal: How has the acid-base concept been expanded?

Instructional Objectives

Students will be able to:
1. Define a Brønsted-Lowry acid as a proton, or H^+, donor.
2. Define a Brønsted-Lowry base as a proton, or H^+, acceptor.
3. Identify the Brønsted-Lowry acids and bases in a given chemical equation.
4. Identify both Brønsted-Lowry and Lewis theories as being more general, or broader, theories than the Arrhenius theory.

Motivation for the Topic

Pour concentrated HCl and concentrated NH_3 solutions into separate 150-mL beakers, and place them next to each other. (Alternatively, cut a 1- to 2-inch-diameter hole in the side of a small carton. Place the two beakers in the carton and cover it. You will soon be able to blow "smoke rings" by pressing on the cover.) Smoke begins to form above the two solutions. What is reacting? Both HCl and NH_3 are gaseous compounds, so the reaction is $HCl\ (g) + NH_3\ (g) \rightarrow NH_4Cl\ (s)$. HCl was previously identified as an acid, and NH_3 as a base, but is this an acid-base reaction? There are no OH^- ions.

Development of the Topic

Remind students that the Arrhenius definition applied to aqueous solutions only. In order to use the terms "acid" and "base" in other media, a new set of definitions was needed. One of these is called the Brønsted-Lowry definition.

Present the definition, and show how in the reaction above, the HCl transfers its proton to the NH_3. Show how in the equation

$$HCl + H_2O \rightarrow H_3O^+ + OH^-$$

HCl is the acid, while H_2O is the base. Show that in the equation

$$NH_3 + H_2O \rightarrow NH_4^+ + OH^-$$

ammonia is the base, while water is the acid. How can water be an acid in one reaction but a base in another? In Brønsted-Lowry theory, the statement "HCl is an acid in water" means the same as "Water is a base in HCl." We call ammonia a base, because, living on a watery planet, we use water as our basis of comparison. Present a few more equations, and have students identify the acids and bases. You may choose to present the conjugate acid-base concept at this time.

If you wish to introduce Lewis theory, mix dilute HCl with a solution of $AgNO_3$ to precipitate AgCl. Add concentrated NH_3, and stir until the precipitate disappears. Write the equation

$$AgCl\ (s) + 2\ NH_3\ (aq) \rightarrow Ag(NH_3)_2^+\ (aq) + Cl^-\ (aq)$$

In this reaction the NH_3 does not form OH^- ions, and does not accept protons. Yet in a third acid-base theory, called Lewis theory, the ammonia is still acting as a base. Lewis defines a base as an electron pair donor, and an acid as an electron pair acceptor.

Show how the Ag^+ ion accepts the lone pair on the NH_3 molecule. Elicit that the Lewis theory is the broadest of the three concepts. Conclude by asking students which definition they prefer, and have them defend their choices.

Suggested Laboratory Activities

I devote more laboratory time to this topic than to any other, often as many as five 40-minute lab periods. This means that the class is still performing acid-base experiments long after they have completed the written material. I believe that the topic offers the opportunity to perform meaningful experiments that the students actually understand and enjoy.

1–3. Qualitative Analysis of Acids and Bases

This is a three-period activity designed by the author.

1. Identification of Four Acids: HCl, H_2SO_4, HNO_3, and $HC_2H_3O_2$

Students are given samples of the four acids, in concentrations of about 0.10 molar. They test these with litmus, pH paper, $AgNO_3$ solution, and $BaCl_2$ solution. (Make sure that the test tubes in which the tests are performed are thoroughly rinsed after the $AgNO_3$ test) On the basis of their observations they are asked how they could identify HNO_3 if the four bottles are unlabeled. Students work in pairs in this activity.

2. Identification of four bases: $NH_3(aq)$, NaOH, $Ca(OH)_2$, $Ba(OH)_2$.

As in the first activity, students test the four solutions with litmus and with pH paper; you may wish them to use phenolphthalein as well. The solutions are then each treated with dilute H_2SO_4, and using fresh samples in clean test tubes, with Na_2CO_3 solution. On the basis of their observations the students are asked how they could identify the NaOH if the four bottles are unlabeled.

3. Identification of Acids and Bases

After the second activity, the students are told that the following week they will be given eight unlabeled bottles containing the four acids and the four bases they have tested. Each team must design a procedure that they will use to identify the eight solutions. Once they have shown the teacher their procedure, they are permitted to follow that procedure, and to identify the eight solutions. My experience is that 90 percent of my groups get all eight right, and the student response to the experiment is overwhelmingly positive.

4. **Determination of the Concentration of an Unknown NaOH Solution Through Titration**

This is a standard activity found in nearly all lab manuals.

5. **pH and Indicators**

If you are able to provide a wide enough range of indicators, students can use them to determine the pH of several unknown substances. Have them fill out a grid like the one below for each unknown. (Give them the range of each indicator.)

Indicator	pH Range	Colors	Result	Conclusion: pH is:
Cresol red*	1–2	red–yellow	yellow	>2
Cresol red	7–8.8	yellow–red	yellow	<7
Methyl orange	3.2–4.4	pink–yellow	yellow	>4.5
Bromthymol blue	6.0–7.6	yellow–blue	yellow	<6
Phenolphthalein	8.2–10	colorless–pink	colorless	<8.2
Alizarin yellow	10–12	yellow–red	yellow	<10
Unknown number ____		Estimate of pH to nearest whole number		5

*Note that cresol red has two pH ranges. It is red below pH 1, yellow from 2 to 7, and then red above 8.8.

13

Redox and Electrochemistry

INTRODUCTION

This chapter again accommodates those who wish to present a less quantitative treatment of the material, by moving the more quantitative material to the end of the chapter. While the course of a replacement reaction is related to the E^0 for the reaction, it can also be predicted from a simple activity series. Both approaches are presented, but the discussion of electrode potentials has been moved to the "Taking a Closer Look" section.

The use of the terms *oxidizing agent* and *reducing agent* has also been postponed to the end of the chapter. The terms often impede students' initial understanding of the concepts of reduction and oxidation, and so might be better reserved for later introduction. In addition, some college texts are now using the terms *oxidant* and *reductant* to replace the *agents*.

Day	Lesson for the Day	Text Pages	Homework
1	Defining reduction and oxidation	440 to 444	Pg. 447, Practice 13.1
2	Analyzing redox reactions	444 to 447	Pgs. 447–448, Practice 13.2–13.5
3	Predicting redox reactions	448 to 450	Pg. 450, Practice 13.6,13.7
4–5	Voltaic cell	451 to 457	Pg. 455, Practice 13.8–13.10
6	Electrolysis	457 to 462	Pg. 459, Practice 13.11
7	Balancing redox reactions	462 to 466	Pg. 466, Practice 13.12, 13.13

Topic I Redox Reactions (3 days)

Goal: How do we use the concept of electron transfer to analyze chemical reactions?

Instructional Objectives

Students will be able to:
1. Define reduction and oxidation in terms of both electron transfer and oxidation state.

2. Find the reduction and oxidation half-reactions within a redox reaction.
3. Complete reduction and oxidation half-reactions by introducing the correct number of electrons to the correct side of the chemical equation.
4. Use a table of chemical activities to predict whether a given redox reaction will occur.
5. Write and correctly balance simple replacement reactions when given the reactants.

Motivation for the Topic

Show the class a piece of rusty iron, and ask what has happened to the iron. Elicit that the iron has been oxidized; it has combined with oxygen. Write the equation for the reaction, and elicit a definition of oxidation. Students will probably define oxidation as "combining with oxygen."

Burn a piece of magnesium ribbon, and ask the students to describe the reaction. Then tell them that in fact, some of the magnesium combines with nitrogen.

$$3 \text{ Mg} + \text{N}_2 \rightarrow \text{Mg}_3\text{N}_2$$

Is this still oxidation? Chemists have extended the definition of oxidation, so that it no longer requires the presence of oxygen.

Development of the Topic

Show that both magnesium and iron lose electrons in the reactions above. Define oxidation as the loss of electrons. Elicit that in both cases, the metal went from neutral to positive; its charge increased. An increase in charge always indicates oxidation. Write the following reaction on the board:

$$2 \text{ SO}_2 + \text{O}_2 \rightarrow 2 \text{ SO}_3$$

The SO_2 is combining with oxygen. Is this also oxidation? Remind the students that although SO_2 is *not* ionic, we can assign sulfur an oxidation state of +4. (This assumes that oxidation numbers were presented previously.) The sulfur in the SO_3 is +6. An increase in oxidation state always indicates oxidation.

When the magnesium, iron, or sulfur loses electrons, what happens to the other element in the equation? Elicit that the other element gains electrons. What is this process called? Other than to deliberately confuse students, why would a process involving the gain of electrons be called "reduction"? Show that in each case, the charge or oxidation number decreases during reduction. Since every oxidation is accompanied by a reduction, chemists refer to reactions involving electron transfer as redox reactions.

A pretty demonstration you may wish to use at this time is the "silver tree." Insert a glass rod into a large one-holed stopper. Wrap thin strips of copper around the glass rod. As you work up from the stopper, the length of the strips should shorten gradually, forming a "tree" of copper metal. Place the tree in a battery jar, and add sufficient silver nitrate solution to cover all of the copper metal. Before showing it to the class, give it one day to react.

Place a piece of copper in a solution of silver nitrate. Write the formula for each reactant on the board. Have students predict the products, and then ask them what has happened to the oxidation number of silver and copper. Emphasize that the copper atoms are oxidized, while the silver 1+ *ions* are reduced. What happened to the nitrate ions in this reaction? Nothing happened to them; they are spectator ions, and the reaction can be written without them:

$$Cu\ (s) + 2\ Ag^+\ (aq) \rightarrow Cu^{2+}\ (aq) + 2\ Ag\ (s)$$

This is called the net ionic equation. Would it still be a balanced equation if we wrote it as follows?

$$Cu\ (s) + Ag^+\ (aq) \rightarrow Cu^{2+}\ (aq) + Ag\ (s)$$

Why not? Emphasize that an ionic equation must be balanced for *charge.*

Define a *half-reaction* as either the oxidation or the reduction taken by itself. Why is it called a half-reaction? Have students write the half-reactions for the replacement reaction above.

Write the following reaction on the board:

$$2\ NaBr + Cl_2 \rightarrow 2\ NaCl + Br_2$$

Ask students to determine the charge of each element in the reaction. What is being oxidized? Make sure your students know that it is Br^- that is oxidized, and *not* Br. What is being reduced? Which is the spectator ion? Students should write the two half-reactions and the net ionic equation. Have your students similarly analyze several additional redox reactions.

Place zinc strips in solutions of silver nitrate, copper(II) nitrate, and magnesium nitrate. Ask students to explain the results, and write the *net* chemical equations. Why did no reaction occur in the magnesium nitrate solution? How can we predict whether a replacement reaction occurs spontaneously?

Show the students an activity series, such as that in Appendix 4, Table J. Why did zinc react with silver ions and copper ions, but not with magnesium ions? Elicit that in general, a metal will react with the ions of a *less* active metal. It will not react with the ions of a *more* active metal. Which other ions would react with zinc? What other metals would react with magnesium ions? What will happen if a piece of magnesium is placed in a solution of $ZnCl_2$? Write the half-reactions and the net ionic equation.

Show that a tiny crystal of solid iodine colors a solution of perchlorethylene pink. Show that a solution of KI (*aq*) mixed with perchlorethylene is colorless. Elicit that while I_2 has a color, I^- ions do not. Ask students to predict what will happen if chlorine is added to the KI solution mixed with perchlorethylene. (Ordinary chlorine bleach works; freshly prepared chlorine water works better.) Elicit that chlorine reacts with iodide ions because chlorine is more active than iodine. What other halide should react with chlorine? (The reaction of chlorine water with NaBr and perchlorethylene should produce a yellow to orange-brown color.)

Topic II *Electricity and Chemical Reactions (3 days)*

Goal: How is electricity obtained from a redox reaction?

Instructional Objectives

Students will be able to:
1. Draw a typical voltaic cell.
2. Predict the direction of electron flow in a given voltaic cell.
3. Identify the anode, cathode, positive pole, and negative pole in a given voltaic cell.
4. Describe the role of the salt bridge in a typical wet cell.
5. Write the appropriate half-reactions that occur at each electrode in the cell.
6. Predict that the voltage becomes zero when the cell reaches equilibrium.
7. Recognize that an electrolytic cell is driven by electricity, while a voltaic cell produces electricity.
8. Identify the half-reactions occurring at each pole in the electrolysis of a molten binary salt.
9. Explain why the anode is positive, and the cathode negative, in an electrolytic cell.
10. Predict the processes occurring at the positive and the negative poles in electroplating.

Motivation for the Topic

Show the class an ordinary flashlight battery. Which side is the negative pole, and which is the positive pole? What do the charges mean? (They indicate the direction of electron flow when the battery is connected to a complete circuit.) What causes the flow of electrons?

Development of the Topic

Remind students that to use a battery, electrons must flow through a wire. What type of reaction involves a flow of electrons? Select a suitable redox reaction, such as $Zn + Cu^{2+}$, and elicit that electrons flow from the zinc atoms to the copper ions.

Set up a voltaic cell like the one shown in Figure 13-1 of the text, but without a salt bridge. For the electrons to go from the zinc to the copper ions, they must now flow through the wire. Attach a voltmeter to the circuit; it shows that there is no voltage. Why not? If the solutions are not connected, the electron flow would cause an imbalance of charge in each beaker. Illustrate that the formation of zinc ions produces excess positive charge, while the disappearance of copper ions produces excess negative ions.

To maintain neutrality, the two solutions must be connected with a device called a salt bridge. (A piece of filter paper, or even paper toweling, soaked in saturated KNO_3 can be used as the salt bridge.) Explain how the flow of ions through the salt bridge completes the circuit, maintaining neutral charge in both beakers. Add the salt bridge to the set-up, and students should be able to see the voltmeter's needle move.

In a battery, we call the pole from which the electrons flow the *negative* pole. Elicit that in the *voltaic* cell you have constructed, the zinc is the negative pole. The electrons flow to the copper, which is therefore the positive pole.

Have students suggest the half-reactions occurring at each pole. Have students define the pole at which oxidation takes place as the anode and the pole where reduction occurs as the cathode. In this case, the zinc is the negative anode.

What happens to a battery, as it is used, over time? Why does the voltage eventually decrease to zero? When the reaction reaches equilibrium, there is no further transfer of electrons.

As a summarizing activity, provide a second cell, with two different metals in solution with their ions. I usually use a Pb/Pb^{2+} half-cell connected to Ag/Ag^+, using an old quarter (1964 or older) as the silver electrode. Have students draw a diagram of the cell, and indicate the direction of electron flow, as well as the charges on the two electrodes. What would happen if we used a dime as the silver electrode instead of the quarter? The size of the electrode has no effect on the voltage. Illustrate this point by having a student read the voltage from both a D battery and an AA battery. (Make sure that both batteries are the same type; if one is rechargeable and the other is not, they will not list the same voltages.)

To motivate a lesson on electrolytic cells, discuss the importance of a given nonspontaneous reaction, such as the decomposition of water as a source of hydrogen gas. Hydrogen gas is used in fuel cells, which are becoming more and more important as possible substitutes for gasoline in automobiles. An alternative, which is my preference, is to throw a piece of sodium in water. **(CAUTION: Be sure to move the students to a safe distance, or use a glass safety shield.)**

You may continue the discussion with the following story. Paul, a high school student, wanted to get some sodium and try this on his own. However, his teacher was wise enough not to give out sodium. Is there a way that Paul could make some? What common substance contains sodium? Can sodium be extracted from $NaCl$?

The reaction

$$2\ NaCl \rightarrow 2\ Na + Cl_2$$

is not spontaneous at temperatures below 5000°C. However, in this reaction, electrons are transferred from the chloride ion to the sodium ion. Show the two half-reactions, and ask, "How can we push electrons in a given direction?" A strong enough battery will force electrons to flow away from its negative pole, into the sodium ions, and will pull electrons from the chloride ions, toward its positive pole. Draw a diagram showing an electrolytic cell, as in Figure 13-3. Use a chart, or table, to list the processes that occur at each pole. Under "negative" for example, you might list:

1. Attracts the positive ions.
2. Positive ions are reduced.
3. Cathode.
4. Electrons flow *away* from the negative pole of the power source.

Why was Paul still unable to produce any sodium in his home laboratory? What must be done to the NaCl to make it conduct electricity? The melting point of sodium is 800°C, too hot to be feasible with ordinary equipment. Students may suggest that he could dissolve the NaCl in water, since aqueous NaCl does conduct electricity. Illustrate why the electrolysis of salt water does not produce sodium. The reduction of water occurs instead.

$$2\ H_2O + 2\ e^- \rightarrow 2\ H_2 + OH^-$$

With a gifted class, you might perform the electrolysis of a solution of dilute sulfuric acid using copper electrodes. Bubbles form at the negative electrode, not at the positive. Ask students to suggest what might be happening. Given enough time, the solution turns blue. What is turning the solution blue? The net reaction is

$$2\ H^+ + Cu \rightarrow Cu^{2+} + H_2$$

Topic III *Balancing Redox Equations (1 day, or 2 days if you wish to permit students to practice their technique. The practice lesson lends itself well to cooperative approaches.)*

Goal: How do we balance redox equations?

Instructional Objectives

Given a redox equation, students will be able to:
1. Write the oxidation and reduction half-reactions.
2. Balance the two half-reactions.

3. Use appropriate coefficients to make the electrons lost equal the electrons gained.

4. Balance the entire equation.

Motivation for the Topic

Perform a colorful redox reaction. For example, add dilute H_2SO_4 to a dilute solution of $KMnO_4$. Pour the solution quickly into a beaker containing a solution of $FeSO_4$, $SnSO_4$, or K_2SO_3. What happened? Recall that when transition metals change oxidation states, they change color. Write the reaction on the board, e.g.,

$$FeSO_4 + H_2SO_4 + KMnO_4 \rightarrow H_2O + K_2SO_4 + MnSO_4 + Fe_2(SO_4)_3$$

This is a very typical redox reaction. How shall we balance it?

Development of the Topic

Because redox reactions are often difficult to balance by inspection, chemists have come up with various methods to help them. One such method uses the oxidation numbers of the products and reactants. In most redox reactions, there is a change in the oxidation number of two elements. Why must two elements change oxidation state? (You can deal with exceptions to this rule, such as the reaction of Cl_2 in water, later.) Elicit that there must be both oxidation and reduction. The number of electrons lost in the oxidation must equal the number gained in the reduction. Provide the oxidation numbers of Fe and Mn at this time. Have students write the two half-reactions:

$$Mn^{7+} + 5e^- \rightarrow Mn^{2+}$$

$$Fe^{2+} \rightarrow Fe^{3+} + e^-$$

Since the iron appears as Fe_2 in the product, it is a good idea to include the "2" in the iron half reaction:

$$2\ Fe^{2+} \rightarrow 2\ Fe^{3+} + 2e^-$$

Show that to make the electrons lost equal the electrons gained, the reduction equation must be multiplied by 2, and the oxidation by 5. Show that putting the numbers back into the original equation gives you

$$10\ FeSO_4 + H_2SO_4 + 2\ KMnO_4 \rightarrow H_2O + K_2SO_4 + 2\ MnSO_4 + 5\ Fe_2(SO_4)_3$$

Now you should be able to elicit that there are 18 sulfates in the product, so that an 8 is needed in front of the H_2SO_4. This requires 8 waters, to balance the hydrogen. The equation is balanced. Check each element to prove that it is balanced. Illustrate how much clearer the reaction becomes when the spectator ions are omitted. Provide several examples to be balanced, but keep the first few as simple as possible!

Suggested Laboratory Activities

1. Determination of the Activity Series

This can be approached in several ways. One method is to provide strips of zinc, lead, and copper, along with nitrate solutions of zinc, lead, copper, and silver. Label the metals, but present the solutions as unknowns. Tell the students that their task is to determine which of the solutions contains zinc ions, which contains lead ions, which contains copper ions, and which contains silver ions. Require that they write out their procedure before beginning the experiment. (Other metals and solutions can be used as well; pretest them to be sure that the desired reactions are observable!)

2. Distinguish Between Halides

A solution of chlorine water can similarly be used to distinguish among chlorides, bromides, and iodides. A few drops of perchlorethylene should be added to each solution to make the results more evident.

3. Setting up Voltaic Cells

Students properly connect various labeled half-cells and record the resulting voltage for several combinations. They are then given an unknown half-cell, containing an unknown metal in a solution of its ions. They are asked to determine its identity by connecting it to the known half-cells.

If they have learned how to calculate E^0, they can use a table of standard reduction potentials to identify the unknown. However, they can identify the unknown without using electrode potentials, by recording the direction of electron transfer for each half-cell combination, and using the activity series.

Students first observe that in any of the voltaic cells they construct, the more active metal is the negative pole. Then by observing the polarities each time the unknown half-cell is connected to the known half-cells, they can place the unknown in its proper position in the activity series and guess its possible identity.

14 *Organic Chemistry*

INTRODUCTION

There seems to be more disagreement over how much time to spend on organic chemistry than there is over any other major topic. One could argue for anything from three days to three months, although two weeks seems to be the norm. The text covers hydrocarbons, nomenclature, functional groups, and a few important reactions. The "Taking a Closer Look" section delves more deeply into the chemistry of the functional groups.

Day	Lesson for the Day	Text Pages	Homework.
1–2	Hydrocarbons	488 to 494	Pg. 494, Practice 14.1, 14.2
3	Nomenclature	494 to 501	Pg. 501, Practice 14.3–14.5
4–5	Functional groups	495 to 496, 502 to 510	Pgs. 506–507, Practice 14.6–14.8
6	Addition and substitution	510 to 512	Pg. 512, Practice 14.9
7–9	Other organic reactions	512 to 519	Pgs. 519–520, Practice 14.10–14.12

Topic I *Hydrocarbons (2 days)*

Goal: What are the structures of the simplest organic compounds?

Instructional Objectives

Students will be able to:
1. Identify a hydrocarbon as a compound that contains only hydrogen and carbon.
2. Draw the structure of a hydrocarbon, given the name.
3. Provide the name of a hydrocarbon, given the structure.
4. Given its formula, place a hydrocarbon in the correct homologous group.
5. Given the number of carbons, predict the number of hydrogen atoms in an alkane, alkene, or alkyne.

Motivation for the Topic

As the class the following questions.

What gas do laboratory burners and your stoves at home use? (Methane, which students should know is CH_4.)

What gas is used in gas-fired backyard barbecues? (Propane, which contains only the elements carbon and hydrogen.)

Hold up a disposable cigarette lighter. What is the liquid in this cigarette lighter? (Butane, which contains only carbon and hydrogen.)

You have probably also heard of octane. What do all of these compounds have in common? (They all contain only carbon and hydrogen, all end in -*ane,* and all are combustible.)

Carbon forms hundreds of thousands of different compounds with hydrogen. In addition, it forms millions of other compounds. The chemistry of carbon is called organic chemistry.

Development of the Topic

How do organic chemicals differ from inorganic chemicals? Demonstrate that organic compounds are generally combustible, that many of them are volatile liquids or soft solids. Relate these properties to the nature of carbon—with an electronegativity of 2.5, it nearly always forms covalent bonds and molecular compounds.

You might wish to discuss the history of the term "organic." Until the mid-nineteenth century, chemists believed that living things could produce substances that could not be synthesized from nonliving material. This "vital force theory" was eventually disproved, and today we call most carbon compounds "organic" whether they are from living things or not.

Why does carbon form so many compounds? Illustrate that carbon always forms four covalent bonds, and that it readily bonds to itself. Draw the structures of methane, propane, and butane. Provide large molecular models, so that students can observe the true three-dimensional shapes.

Elicit that these are all called hydrocarbons, because they contain only hydrogen and carbon. With so many compounds possible, a special system was designed to name the hydrocarbons. Show the derivation of the name propane, pointing out that *prop-* means three carbons, and -*ane* means single bonds.

Elicit the meanings of the prefixes *meth-, but-,* and *oct-.* List the prefixes indicating from 1 to 10 carbons. (I allow students to refer to the list during exams, to reduce the amount of memorization in the topic.)

Elicit the formulas of ethane and pentane, and elicit the general formula, C_nH_{2n+2}. Show that each compound differs from the next by the same formula, CH_2. Define the "Alkane family" as the group of hydrocarbons containing only single bonds, with the general formula C_nH_{2n+2}. Ask your students to draw and provide the formulas for a few additional alkanes, such as hexane and nonane.

Ask students if they have heard the term "polyunsaturated," and ask what it means. Point out that in organic chemistry, unsaturated means having double or triple carbon-carbon bonds. What, then, would polyunsaturated mean? Draw two carbons, connected by a double bond. Elicit that the double bond leaves room for only four hydrogen atoms. Remind students that ethane has six hydrogen atoms. Alkanes are called saturated hydrocarbons. How is the use of the word "saturated" in organic chemistry related to the way the word is used to describe certain solutions?

Tell the class that the compound C_2H_4 is called ethene, and is the simplest of the alkenes. Elicit the general formula of the alkene series. Have students draw the structures of propene and butene. If students notice that there are two different ways to draw butene, you may wish to introduce the concept of isomerism.

Tell the class that the simplest triple-bonded hydrocarbon is called ethyne. Have them draw it, suggest a general formula, and then draw at least two additional alkynes, checking that they follow the general formula. Throughout the topic of organic chemistry, whenever possible, provide three-dimensional models of the compounds illustrated on the board.

If your students drew the two different butene structures, it provides a nice lead-in to a discussion of nomenclature. These are different compounds; therefore, they must have different names. Define isomers, and show why these are called 1-butene and 2-butene. Show why there is no 3-butene.

Present the rules for naming hydrocarbons. (See pages 498–499.) Provide plenty of examples, including the 3-methylpentane diagram shown on page 499. Students will often call it 2-ethylbutane, and it is important to show them why this is incorrect. By using a molecular model you can make it clear that no matter how you draw it, the longest chain has five carbons. In general, however, draw the longest chain straight across, rather than being tricky by bending it. Since we do not attempt to show the correct bond angles when we draw these organic structures, we might as well simplify the naming process by making the main chain the one that goes left to right across the page.

For extra credit you might ask your students to draw and name as many isomers of octane as they can.

Topic II *Functional Groups (2–3 days)*

Goal: What is the chemistry of some other (i.e., other than hydrocarbons) common organic compounds?

Instructional Objectives

Students will be able to:

1. Classify a given compound according to its functional group.
2. Name simple compounds containing the functional groups discussed.
3. Recognize isomerism in compounds containing different functional groups, e.g., aldehydes and ketones.
4. Given the name of the compound, draw compounds containing the listed functional groups.

Motivation for the Topic

Provide bottles of ethanol and of rubbing alcohol, 2-propanol. Do not tell the students what is in the bottles, but ask them to identify them by their odor. Students will generally identify both compounds as alcohol. Point out that they are in fact both alcohols, but "alcohol" refers not to just one compound, but to an entire class of compounds.

Show that in alcohols an —OH group has replaced one or more hydrogens in a hydrocarbon. The alcohols resemble each other in many ways, so it is useful to group them. The functional group concept helps us to group similar compounds.

Development of the Topic

Use the alcohols to illustrate how compounds containing functional groups are named. Make sure that your students can correctly name simple alcohols, such as 3-pentanol, and given the name, can draw the structure. Show that alcohols have the general formula R—OH. Use a conductivity apparatus to demonstrate that alcohols do not conduct electricity. Show that a solution of NaOH does conduct. Why is this? Make sure that your students realize that alcohols do *not* form hydroxide ions, and therefore are not bases.

Similarly, go through the remaining functional groups described on pages 502 to 506. (Note that esters are described later in the chapter, under "Esterification.") If you wish to provide a more expanded presentation, you can include more of the chemistry of each group, as shown on pages 520 to 529.

As your class goes through drawing and naming the compounds containing the groups described, take the opportunity to illustrate isomerism. For example, we observed earlier that propanol has an isomer, but does ethanol have an isomer? Show that dimethyl ether is an isomer of ethanol; all ethers have alcohol isomers. The same is true of ketones and aldehydes, and esters and acids.

Molecular model kits are useful in demonstrating isomerism; for example, have a student take apart a ketone and put it together as an alcohol.

Topic III *Reactions in Organic Chemistry (2–3 days)*

Goal: What are some types of organic reactions?

Instructional Objectives

Students will be able to:
1. Identify seven types of organic reactions, given the reactants and products.
2. Given the reactants, predict products of those reactions.
3. Identify and name esters, and identify the parent acid and alcohol for a given ester.

Motivation for the Topic

Show empty bottles of various alcoholic beverages. Point out that the alcohol is ethanol. Where do we get alcohol? Students will probably know that alcohol is made from grapes, but point out that the alcohol in rum comes from molasses; alcohol can be made from corn, rye, potatoes, or barley. All these plants contain sugars, and from sugars we can produce alcohol.

Development of the Topic

Write the equation for the following reaction:

$$C_6H_{12}O_6 \rightarrow 2\ CO_2 + 2\ C_2H_5OH$$

Place some sugar in water, and ask whether it will eventually turn to alcohol. Why not? The reaction is very slow; it requires a catalyst. Students may know that yeasts are used to catalyze the reaction; they may also know that the reaction is called anaerobic respiration, and provides energy for the yeast cells. The sugar ferments, to form ethanol and carbon dioxide. The reaction is called fermentation.

Fill one small gas-collecting jar with butane and another with ethyne, or any other unsaturated, gaseous hydrocarbon available. Place a glass plate over each jar. Invert a jar of Br_2 vapor over each jar of gas, forming two sets of two jars. Remove the glass plate from between each set. The unsaturated hydrocarbon immediately reacts with the bromine, causing a dramatic loss of color, while nothing happens in the other set of jars. Point out that the same results would occur with nearly any saturated and unsaturated hydrocarbons. They react differently. Why?

Show that when bromine reacts with butane, a C—H bond breaks. These bonds are strong, so the reactions are very slow. Illustrate the following reaction using molecular models:

$$C_4H_{10} + Br_2 \rightarrow C_4H_9Br + HBr$$

Show why the reaction is called substitution, emphasizing that it always forms two products. Show that the reaction can form a large number of different organic compounds, since it is difficult to control how often the bromine molecules will substitute onto a given compound.

Why does an unsaturated hydrocarbon react so much faster? Compare 1-butene with butane. They must react differently because one has a C—C double bond, and the other does not. Point out that it is easier to break a C—C double bond than it is to break the C—H bond. (If you covered the concepts of sigma and pi bonding, you can provide a better explanation. The pi bond is more reactive than the sigma bond.)

Draw the structure of 1-butene, and then erase the double bond, leaving a single bond in that position. What happens now? There are now two adjoining carbons each with only 3 bonds. Each can take a bromine atom, producing 1,2-dibromobutane. What would happen if we reacted bromine with 2-butene?

If you intend to teach about benzene rings and aromatic hydrocarbons, this is a good time. Benzene is unsaturated, yet it reacts by substitution. Why is this? See the Box Feature "Lord of the Rings" on pages 535 to 537.

Polymerization can be introduced as a type of addition reaction. Condensation polymers are produced through the removal of water, which your students may recognize as dehydration synthesis.

Esterification reactions can be demonstrated. Add solid salicylic acid to methanol, in a large Erlenmeyer flask. Add one or two drops of concentrated sulfuric acid. Place the flask on a hot plate, swirling it occasionally. When it begins to boil, remove it from the hot plate and quickly add some cold water. A white solid will form that has the characteristic odor of wintergreen.

While the reaction is taking place, ask the students what might happen when an alcohol, ROH, reacts with an acid, RCOOH. Use molecular models of a simple alcohol and a simple acid to illustrate what happens when a water is removed. Attach the remaining pieces, to form an ester. Show that the general formula for the ester is RCOOR'. Show how to name the ester that you have formed. Esters can be described as "alkyl alkanoate." The part that came from the alcohol comes first in the name. If students ask about the logic of the naming system, point out that the -ate ending is analogous to the way salts are named.

Have the students smell the ester that you have produced. Point out that esters are responsible for the fragrances and flavors of bananas, pears, and other fruit.

Remind students that bases feel slippery to the touch. Point out that strong bases react with animal fats to produce soaps, which feel slippery. The reaction is called soap making, or saponification. Provide the typical saponification reaction, as shown on page 517, and summarize it by showing that a fat reacts with lye to produce a soap and glycerol.

The combustion of hydrocarbons was discussed at the beginning of the chapter. Ask students to write the equation for the combustion of methane.

Ask the class: What are the products? Why should you know them? (If the reaction produced CO instead of CO_2, the fumes from the stove would be lethal.) Show that such compounds as ethanol and acetone are also combustible, and form the same products. What use has been suggested for the combustion of ethanol? (It could be used to power automobiles.)

Suggested Laboratory Activity

Construction of Molecular Models

Groups of students are given molecular model kits, and asked to construct and then draw models of several organic compounds. The concept of cis-trans isomerism across double bonds can be developed during this lab, by including 1,2-dichloroethene as one of the substances. The models can be used to answer questions about isomerism and geometry.

15 *Nuclear Chemistry*

INTRODUCTION

The key skills students need to master in nuclear chemistry are writing nuclear equations and solving half-life problems. They typically have little trouble with the first of these, and a lot of trouble with the second. Even when they are given an equation, and they set it up correctly, they are often thrown by the exponential relationship between the number of half-life periods and the fraction remaining. We therefore illustrate two solution methods in our Sample Problems on pages 549 to 552.

Day	Lesson for the Day	Text Pages	Homework
1	What is radioactivity?	538 to 542	
2	Modes of decay	542 to 548	Pgs. 546–547, Practice 15.1–15.2 Pg. 548, Practice 15.3–15.4
3–4	Half-life	548 to 554	Pg. 552, Practice 15.5–15.7
5	Fission and fusion	554 to 557	Pg. 546, Practice 15.8
6	Uses of radioisotopes	557 to 559	

Topic I *Natural Radiation (2 days)*

Goal: How do we explain the phenomenon called radioactivity?

Instructional Objectives

Students will be able to:
1. Describe radioactivity as the emission of matter and energy from unstable nuclei.
2. Distinguish among alpha, beta, and gamma emissions, in terms of charge, mass, and penetrating power.
3. Complete nuclear equations from which a single term is omitted.
4. Write the equation for the radioactive decay of a given nuclide, based on a given decay mode.
5. Identify elements with atomic numbers of 84 or greater as radioactive elements.

Motivation for the Topic

Henri Becquerel, a French scientist, noticed that a certain rock, called pitchblende, had an unusual property. Photographic film stored next to pitchblende exhibited streaks, as if it had been exposed to light. The rock did not produce any visible light, yet it affected the film. Becquerel concluded that there were some kind of invisible rays being emitted by the pitchblende. What do you think was happening? (If students have trouble figuring it out, tell them that pitchblende contains uranium.)

Development of the Topic

Show students that when radiation passes between charged plates, it splits into three parts. (See Figure 15-1 in text.) Elicit the charge of each type of radiation, and present the names alpha, beta, and gamma. Prepare a chart, or table, comparing the three "rays" in terms of charge, mass, and penetrating power.

State that many elements are naturally radioactive, and elicit the names of some of these elements. Where are they found on the Periodic Table? Students should conclude that the elements with the largest nuclei tend to be radioactive. Point out that every element with at least 84 protons is always radioactive. Nuclei with 84 or more protons are unstable. Which of the three types of radiation discussed would best relieve an overcrowded nucleus?

What happens to an element when it emits an alpha particle? Show that ^{238}U changes into ^{234}Th, and write the balanced nuclear equation. Emphasize that nuclear equations must obey the laws of conservation of mass and of charge. Have the class complete the nuclear equation for alpha emission for some other isotopes, such as radium-226 or francium-220.

Introduce the concept of radioactive dating. Some students have probably learned that carbon-14 is used to date the remains of living things. Why is ^{14}C radioactive? Neither ^{13}C nor ^{12}C is radioactive. Apparently, carbon-14 has too many neutrons. Point out that for the first 20 elements, the ratio of neutrons to protons is generally very close to 1.0. If the ratio is too large, the nucleus is radioactive. How can a nucleus solve its "problem" of too many neutrons? Write the nuclear equation for beta emission in ^{14}C. Elicit that the number of neutrons has decreased, while the number of protons has increased. Show that the process of beta emission, in general, can be represented by the following equation:

$$\, _0^1n \rightarrow \, _1^1p + \, _{-1}^0e$$

A neutron, by emitting a beta particle, is converted into a proton. Provide a table of alpha and beta emitters, such as the one given on page 549. Have students complete nuclear equations for the decay of such isotopes as ^{60}Co, ^{131}I, and ^{222}Rn. Should you wish to include positron emission, illustrate the decay of ^{37}Ca. Students should notice that this isotope has too few neutrons. Show that positron decay results in the conversion of a proton into a neutron, the opposite result of beta decay.

Topic II *Half-Life (2 days)*

Goal: How do we predict the results of radioactive decay?

Instructional Objectives

Students will be able to:

1. Given a half-life, an original quantity, and an amount of time, predict the remaining quantity of a radioactive isotope.
2. Find the half-life of a nuclide, given the original quantity and the quantity remaining after a given amount of time.
3. Predict the amount of time necessary for a given change in mass, given the half-life of the nuclide.
4. Use the equation for half-life to predict quantities going back in time as well as forward.
5. Apply the concept of half-life to radioactive dating.
6. State that the half-life of a given nuclide is constant, unaffected by changes in pressure, quantity, temperature, or chemical environment.

Motivation for the Topic

Let us say that you have been working on your homework for 15 minutes, and your friend asks, "When will you be finished?" You reply, "I'm half done!" What would your friend assume? The conclusion that you will be finished in another 15 minutes is based on the assumption that you are doing homework at a steady rate. Now suppose that you have ordered a large pizza. After 15 minutes, you have eaten half of the pie, or 4 slices. But now you are not as hungry. What is likely to happen in the next 15 minutes? The rate is not likely to be constant! It is going to be difficult to predict how long it will take you to finish. The rate of radioactive decay, like the rate of eating pizza, decreases over time. How will we be able to predict the results?

Development of the Topic

Suppose that as you ate your pizza, your rate became proportional to the number of slices remaining. When there were four slices remaining, you could eat only half as fast as you did when there were eight slices remaining. It took you 15 minutes to eat the first four slices. It would then take you the same amount of time to eat two slices, going from four remaining to two. With two slices left, your rate would be only one fourth of what it was at the beginning. It would take you 15 minutes now to eat just one slice. If we review the results, we see that it took 15 minutes to go from 8 slices to 4, from 4 to 2, and from 2 to 1. Although the rate is not constant, the amount of time it takes to use up half of the sample *is* constant! Radioactive decay follows the same pattern. The amount of time needed to use up half of a given sample is constant. This time is called the *half-life*. The half-life of our pizza was 15 minutes.

Show how half-life periods can be used to predict quantity. Radium-226 is a good isotope to start with, since the half-life is a nice round 1600 years. Review what it means to say that the half-life is 1600 years; what will happen in 1600 years? What would happen in 3200 years? How much of an 8.00-gram sample of ^{226}Ra would remain after 3200 years? (2.00 grams)

One method of helping students arrive at the correct answer to this type of problem is to set up a chart like this one:

Time	Number of Half-life Periods	Mass
0	0	8.00 g
1600	1	4.00 g
3200	2	2.00 g

Point out that although a chart like this can be used to solve problems involving any whole number of half-life periods, when the number gets large, the method becomes tedious. A mathematical expression can be used to predict quantities based on half-life.

$$\text{fraction remaining} = \left(\frac{1}{2}\right)^{\frac{t}{T}}$$

(See text page 548.) In the formula, t is the time elapsed and T is the half-life. The exponent t/T is the number of half-life periods. Show that in the problem above, $t = 3200$ years and T is 1600 years. The exponent t/T is 2, which mean that two half-life periods have passed. The fraction remaining is $\left(\frac{1}{2}\right)^{2}$; or 1/4, therefore, the mass remaining, $mr = 8.00$ g/4 = 2.00 grams. You may wish to point out that t/T does not have to be a whole number. Using a scientific calculator, it is easy to raise $\frac{1}{2}$ to any power.

Provide problems requiring students to find each of the variables in the equation—the half-life, the time, the original mass. Students generally find these difficult, so a period of drill may be needed. One type of problem that often presents difficulty is this: A certain radioactive isotope decays from 64.0 grams to 2.0 grams in 60.0 minutes. What is its half-life? The chart method, shown above, gives

Time	Number of Half-Life Periods	Mass
0	0	64.0
	1	32.0
	2	16.0
	3	8.0
	4	4.0
60.0	5	2.0

The students can now conclude that since 5 half-life periods is 60.0 minutes, the half-life is 12.0 minutes.

However, suppose the students wish to use the equation:

$$\text{fraction remaining} = \left(\frac{1}{2}\right)^{\frac{t}{T}}$$

The fraction remaining is 2 g/64 g or 1/32.

$$\frac{1}{32} = \left(\frac{1}{2}\right)^{\frac{t}{T}}, \ \frac{1}{32} = \left(\frac{1}{2}\right)^{5}$$

$$\frac{t}{T} = 5$$

$$\frac{60}{T} = 5$$

$$T = 12$$

Topic III *Using Radioactive Substances (1 day)*

Goal: How does the use of radioactive materials benefit humanity?

Instructional Objectives

Students will be able to:
1. Describe nuclear fission as a process of obtaining energy by splitting large nuclei.
2. Describe nuclear fusion as a process that produces energy through the combination of small nuclei to produce larger nuclei.
3. Identify fusion as the source of the sun's energy.
4. Describe both the advantages and disadvantages of the use of nuclear power.
5. Describe other uses of radioactive isotopes, such as in shrinking tumors, medical diagnosis, and tracing the course of a chemical reaction.

Motivation

Discuss global warming. Point out that many (but not all) scientists believe that global warming is largely caused by the increase in CO_2 in the atmosphere. Power plants that burn oil, coal, or natural gas, produce carbon dioxide. If we wish to decrease the amount of carbon dioxide while producing the same amount of electrical power, what are our alternatives?

Development of the Topic

Point out that nuclear power plants produce no carbon dioxide. They do not produce any air pollution. Yet no new nuclear plants are being built in the United States. Why is this?

Students will provide their opinion of the dangers of nuclear power. It is important to separate the facts from the fiction!

Show the nuclear equation for the fission of ^{235}U. (See text page 555.) Since the reaction produces more neutrons than it consumes, it is self-sustaining. However, unless a certain minimum quantity and concentration of ^{235}U is present, it is impossible for a nuclear explosion to occur. Point out that the barium-143 and the krypton-90 produced in fission have mass numbers that are much larger than the average atomic mass of those elements. What generally happens when nuclei have an abnormally large number of neutrons? The products of fission are always highly radioactive, and thus dangerous. They must be stored in a safe, secure facility.

You might assign students to prepare a report on the use of nuclear power in other countries. (Both Japan and France rely heavily on nuclear power.)

Ask students where the energy of the sun and other stars comes from. What elements are found on the sun? Show how the fusion of hydrogen atoms produces helium, an element that was found on the sun before it was found on Earth. Fusion produces enormous amounts of energy and no radioactive products. Why do we use fission instead of fusion to supply energy? Point out that the amount of energy necessary to get positively charged nuclei to overcome their repulsions and fuse is so large that it cannot be provided feasibly. An atomic bomb can supply the necessary energy, and so we have built bombs that use fusion—hydrogen bombs—but as yet, we have been unable to use fusion in more peaceful applications.

The graph of nuclear binding energy vs. mass number on page 561 and the concept of mass defect can be used to explain the production of energy in both fission and fusion. Students should understand that mass is lost during both processes and that this mass is converted into energy.

Other uses of radioactivity should be discussed to complete the topic. Students are likely to have heard of radiation therapy and, unfortunately, are likely to know someone who has undergone it. How can radiation be used to cure cancer, when radiation can also cause cancer? While radiation kills normal cells along with malignant cells, it is used only where the potential benefits far outweigh the risks.

The individual instructor should decide the extent to which such applications as irradiation of food, medical diagnosis, tracing, and determination of reaction mechanisms should be discussed. They are good topics for student-led discussions and reports.

Answer Key

CHAPTER 1

Page 7

1.1 Ice is less dense than water. Ice floats on water.

1.2 (a) chemical
(b) physical
(c) physical
(d) chemical
(e) physical

1.3 (a) physical
(b) physical
(c) chemical
(d) chemical
(e) chemical
(f) physical
(g) physical

Page 13

1.4 A compound has been formed through a chemical reaction. The solid is zinc sulfide.

1.5 (a) element
(b) mixture
(c) compound
(d) mixture
(e) mixture
(f) element
(g) compound

1.6 Chemically, they are all the same.

1.7 Water, a compound, and neon, an element, are true substances. Cola, air, and blood are all mixtures.

Page 18

1.8 (a) 2 minutes
(b) 100°

1.9 The higher of the two temperatures where the curve levels out is the boiling point.

1.10 It is a liquid.

1.11 The average kinetic energy is not changing.

Page 22

1.12 $Q = mc \, \Delta t$

$$840. \text{ J} = 40. \text{ g} \times 4.18 \frac{\text{J}}{\text{g} \cdot \text{K}} \times \Delta t$$

$$\frac{840. \text{ J}}{40 \text{ g} \times 4.18 \frac{\text{J}}{\text{g} \cdot \text{K}}} = 5.0 \text{ K}$$

1.13 $Q = mc\Delta t$

$$\text{J} = 20. \text{ g} \times 4.18 \frac{\text{J}}{\text{g} \cdot \text{K}}$$

$$\text{J} = 420 \text{ J}$$

1.14 Endothermic

1.15 $Q = mc\Delta t$

$$\text{J} = 50. \text{ g} \times 4.18 \frac{\text{J}}{\text{g} \cdot \text{K}} \times 40 = 8360$$

$$\text{J} = 8400$$

1.16 $Q = mc\Delta t$

$$8360 \text{ J} = \text{m} \times 4.18 \frac{\text{J}}{\text{g} \cdot \text{K}} \times 10 \text{ K}$$

$$\frac{8360 \text{ J}}{4.18 \frac{\text{J}}{\text{g} \cdot \text{K}} \times 10 \text{ K}} = m = 200 \text{g}$$

1.17 $Q = mc\Delta t$

$$400. = 40.0 \text{g} \times 4.18 \text{ K}$$

$$\frac{400 \text{ J}}{40.0 \text{ g} \times 4.18 \text{ K}} = 2.39 = 2.4 \frac{\text{J}}{\text{g} \cdot \text{K}}$$

Page 23

1.18. $Q = mc\Delta t$

$Q = 10. \times \dfrac{1c}{g \bullet C°} \times 20°C = 200$ cal

1.19 $100{,}000$ cal $= g \times \dfrac{1c}{g \bullet C°} \times 100°C = 1000$ g

1.20 $273 + 100°C = 373$ K

1.21 253 K $- 273 = -20°C$

1.22 27 K

1.23 0.50 atm

Page 33

1.24 $P_1V_1 = P_2V_2$, 2.0 atm $\times 4.0$ L $= P_2 16L = 0.50$ atm

1.25 $P_1V_1 = P_2V_2$, 405.2 kPa $\times 24$ mL $= 101.3$ kPa, $V_2 = 96$ mL

1.26 $P_1V_1 = P_2V_2$, Pressure is halved.

Page 35

1.27 $27°C + 273 = 290$ K

$127°C + 273 = 390$ K

$\dfrac{V_1}{T_1} = \dfrac{V_2}{T_2}$, $\dfrac{30}{290} = \dfrac{V_2}{390} = 40$ mL

1.28 $\dfrac{V_1}{T_1} = \dfrac{V_2}{T_2}$, $\dfrac{40}{364} = \dfrac{V_2}{273} = 30$ mL

1.29 There would be no change.

Page 36

1.30 2 atm; 202.6 kPa

Page 38

1.31 $\dfrac{P_1V_1}{T_1} = \dfrac{P_2V_2}{T_2}$

$\dfrac{240 \text{ mL} \times 2.0 \text{ atm}}{300 \text{ K}} = \dfrac{V_2 \times 4.0 \text{ atm}}{400 \text{ K}} = 160$ mL

1.32 $\dfrac{P_1V_1}{T_1} = \dfrac{P_2V_2}{T_2}$

$\dfrac{25.0 \text{ L} \times 1 \text{ atm}}{300 \text{ K}} = \dfrac{50.0 \text{ L} \times 0.40 \text{ atm}}{T_2}$

$T_2 = \dfrac{50.0 \text{ L} \times 0.40 \text{ atm} \times 300 \text{ K}}{25.0 \text{ L} \times 1 \text{ atm}}$

$= 240$ K

Page 43

1.33 (a) Additional molecules cause more collisions with the walls of the tire, resulting in increased pressure.
(b) Warmer temperatures indicate faster moving molecules. These exert a greater force on the walls of the tire, as they collide with the walls with greater frequency and greater energy. A greater force results in a higher pressure.

1.34 Increased volume (rink size) results in decreased pressure (collisions with walls), the inverse relationship between pressure and volume is Boyle's Law.

Page 46

1.35 0.5 atm

1.36 $\dfrac{0.5}{1.5} = \dfrac{3 \text{ moles}}{m} = 9$ moles O_2

Page 49

1.37 Acetone

1.38 118°C

1.39 71 kPa

1.40 Acetone

1.41 Acetic acid has stronger intermolecular attractions than water. Therefore, it should also have greater surface tension.

1.42 Acetone has week intermolecular attractions. Therefore, it evaporates and dries very quickly. Since evaporation is an endothermic process, the rapid evaporation causes noticeable cooling.

Page 52

1.43 $Q = mhf = 5.00$ g $\times 334 \dfrac{J}{g} = 1670$ J

1.44 $Q = mhv = 10.0$ g $\times 2260 \dfrac{J}{g} = 22{,}600$ J

1.45 $Q = mhf = 5.00 \text{ g} \times 334 \dfrac{J}{g} = 1670 \text{ J}$

1.46 $Q = mhf + mc\Delta t + mh$

$= 2.00 \text{ g} \times 334 \dfrac{J}{g} + 4.18 \dfrac{J}{g \bullet K}$

$100 \text{ K} + 2.00 \text{ g} \times 2260 \dfrac{J}{g}$

$= 6024 \text{ J} = 6020 \text{ J}$

Page 57

1.47 $PV = nRT$

$n = \dfrac{PV}{RT} = \dfrac{1.00 \text{ atm} \times 10. \text{ L}}{0.082 \text{ L atm} \times 300. \text{ K}} =$
$\dfrac{10.00}{0.082 \times 300.} = 0.406 \text{ mole}$

1.48 $P = \dfrac{nRT}{V} = P = \dfrac{4}{2R2}$ No change.

Chapter Review

Page 57

1. (1)	**2.** (3)	**3.** (2)	**4.** (3)
5. (1)	**6.** (3)	**7.** (3)	**8.** (1)
9. (3)	**10.** (2)	**11.** (1)	**12.** (1)
13. (3)	**14.** (1)	**15.** (2)	**16.** (1)
17. (2)	**18.** (3)	**19.** (2)	**20.** (4)
21. (3)	**22.** (3)	**23.** (3)	**24.** (3)
25. (4)	**26.** (2)	**27.** (2)	**28.** (2)
29. (4)	**30.** (1)	**31.** (2)	**32.** (2)
33. (2)	**34.** (1)	**35.** (2)	**36.** (3)
37. (3)	**38.** (1)	**39.** (3)	**40.** (1)

Constructed Response

Page 62

1. 10.0*L* remains in the tank; new pressure is 6 *atm*. A gas occupies the entire volume of its container. When half the gas escapes, there are only half as many collisions.

2. Because mercury has a low vapor pressure, its forces of attraction must be high, its rate of evaporation low, and its boiling point high.

3. (a) $Q = mc\Delta t$,

$Q = 200 \text{ g} \times 4.18 \dfrac{J}{g \bullet K} \times 50 \text{ K} =$
$41{,}800 \text{ J or } 42 \text{ KJ}$

$Q = 200 \text{ g} \times 1 \dfrac{cal}{g° \, C} \times 50 =$
$10{,}000 \text{ cal, or } 10 \text{ kcal}$

(b) $42\text{kJ} = 100.\text{g} \times 4.18 \dfrac{J}{g \bullet K} = \Delta t$

The temperature change should be 100°C. However, once the temperature increases 70°C, the boiling point of water is reached (30°C + 70°C = 100°C). The temperature will remain at 100°C until all the water boils away.

Chemistry Challenge

Page 62

1. (b)
2. (e)
3. (d)
4. (e)
5. (d)
6. (c)
7. (d)
8. (e)
9. (a)
10. (d)
11. (b)
12. (d)

CHAPTER 2

Practice

Page 72

2.1 Thomson thought that atoms of different elements are different. Democritus thought that all atoms were identical.

2.2 Rutherford explained that the atoms are mostly empty space, therefore only a very small number of alpha particles actually struck the nucleus and bounced back.

2.3 14, the number of protons, the atomic number, is the same as the number of electrons in a neutral atom.

2.4 14, the protons and neutrons are in the nucleus.

Page 74

2.5 $0.79 \times 24 = 18.96$, $0.10 \times 25 = 2.5$, $0.11 \times 26 = 2.86$
$18.96 + 2.5 + 2.86 = 24.32$

2.6 (a) 19 protons, 20 neutrons, 19 electrons, 39 nucleons
(b) 6 protons, 8 neutrons, 6 electrons, 14 nucleons
(c) 18 protons, 22 neutrons, 18 electrons, 40 nucleons

Page 79

2.7 Red light contains the smallest amount of energy.

2.8 This is a good analogy. There are only 88 keys on a piano, therefore it plays 88 notes. Although the violin has only four strings, it can play an infinite number of notes as the violinist's bow slides along the strings.

Page 85

2.9

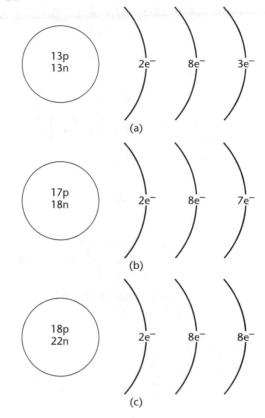

2.10 There are eight electrons in the second principal energy level of silicon.

Page 95

2.11

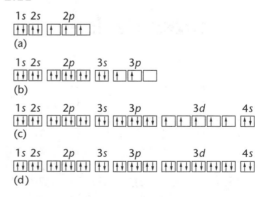

2.12 (a) 2 (b) 3 (c) 0 (d) 6

2.13 (a) Violates Hund's rule

(b) Too many electrons

1s	2s	2p		
↑↓	↑↓	↑↓	↑↓	↑

(c) Violates Pauli Exclusion

1s	2s	2p			3s
↑↑	↑↓	↑↓	↑↓	↑↓	↑↓

(d) Violates Hund's rule

1s	2s	2p		
↑↓	↑↓	↑	↑	↑

Page 99

2.14 (a) 2 unpaired electrons
(b) 1 filled principal energy level
(c) 3 filled orbitals

2.15 (a) 4 unpaired electrons
(b) $1s^2\ 2s^2\ 2p^2$

Page 105

2.16 (a) $1s^2\ 2s^2\ 2p^6\ 3s^2\ 3p^6\ 3d^5\ 4s^2$
(b) $1s^2\ 2s^2\ 2p^6\ 3s^2\ 3p^6\ 3d^{10}\ 4s^2$ $4p^6\ 4d^2\ 5s^2$
(c) $1s^2\ 2s^2\ 2p^6\ 3s^2\ 3p^6\ 3d^{10}\ 4s^1$

Page 107

2.17 (a) 20 electrons
(b) $1s^2\ 2s^2\ 2p^6\ 3s^2\ 3p^6\ 3d^2$

2.18 $1s^2\ 2s^2\ 2p^6\ 3s^2\ 3p^6\ 3d^5$

Chapter Review

Page 107

1. (2)	**2.** (3)	**3.** (3)	**4.** (3)
5. (2)	**6.** (3)	**7.** (4)	**8.** (3)
9. (3)	**10.** (1)	**11.** (1)	**12.** (4)
13. (4)	**14.** (3)	**15.** (1)	**16.** (4)
17. (3)	**18.** (3)	**19.** (4)	**20.** (3)
21. (3)	**22.** (4)	**23.** (4)	**24.** (3)
25. (4)	**26.** (3)	**27.** (2)	**28.** (1)
29. (2)	**30.** (4)	**31.** (1)	**32.** (4)
33. (2)	**34.** (3)	**35.** (1)	**36.** (3)
37. (4)	**38.** (4)		

Constructed Response

Page 111

1. (a) Electronegativity is low because it loses electrons easily. (b) Number of principal energy levels is high, placing the electrons far from the nucleus. (c) Number of valence electrons is low. Atoms with low ionization energies have few valence electrons.

2. Period 3 (a) 8 elements
   (b) 3s and 3p

   Period 5 (a) 18 elements
   (b) 5s, 4d, 5p

   Period 6 (a) 32 elements
   (b) 6s, 4f, 5d, 6p

3. Assertion (a) has been changed. We no longer think of the electron as moving in a fixed path. We identify a region where it spends most of its time. This region is called an orbital.

4. Zn, Cd, Hg, Uub, Pd

Chemistry Challenge

Page 111

1. (3)
2. (4)
3. (3)
4. (2)
5. (3)
6. (3)
7. (2)
8. (2)
9. (1)

CHAPTER 3

Practice

3.1

(a) H:N:H with H below (ammonia Lewis structure)

(b) H:C::O: with H above C

(c) :O::S:O: with :O: below (sulfur trioxide)

(d) :Br:Cl:

(e) :O: with :O: and :O: around (structure)

(f) :N::N:

3.2 H—O, H—I, N—I, Br—Cl

3.3 6 electrons

3.4 One fluorine atom will form a nonpolar covalent bond with another fluorine atom.

Page 1 27

3.5 (a) covalent
(b) covalent
(c) ionic
(d) ionic

3.6 The Na—F bond would have the greater ionic character.

Page 135

3.7 (a) linear, nonpolar—identical atoms

(b) linear, polar—large electronegativity difference

(c) pyramidal, polar—asymmetrical with polar bonding, similar to NH_3

(d) tetrahedral, nonpolar—the molecule is symmetrical, similar to CH_4

(e) linear, nonpolar—polar bonds but a nonpolar molecule because it is symmetrical, similar to CO_2

3.8. The polar molecules HCl *and* PH_3 would behave in a manner similar to water.

Page 141

3.9 (a) HF, because of hydrogen bonds
(b) C_3H_8, because larger molecules have more electrons and stronger dispersion forces
(c) C_2H_5OH, because the —OH group allows for hydrogen bonding

3.10 C_8H_{18} is a covalent compound held by weak intermolecular forces. KF is an ionic compound held by strong ionic bonds.

3.11 Glycerol, with three —OH groups, has a higher molecular weight and more hydrogen bonding than propanol, which has only one —OH group.

Page 143

3.12 A = Mercury—metals are excellent conductors in solid and liquid states

B = Pentane—molecular substances have a low melting point and boiling point

C = $CaBr_2$—ionic solids are good conductors liquid state, poor in solid state

D = Carbon—network solids are poor conductors in all states

E = Calcium—metals are excellent conductors in solid and liquid states

Page 149

3.13 It resembles the sulfate ion, SO_4^{2-} ion.

$$\left[\begin{array}{c} :O: \\ :O:P:O: \\ :O: \end{array} \right]^{3-}$$

3.14 The hybridization is sp^3; there is resonance.

$$:O:$$
$$:S::O:$$

3.15 They have identical structures because they have the same number of electrons, the same hybridization, and the same geometry.

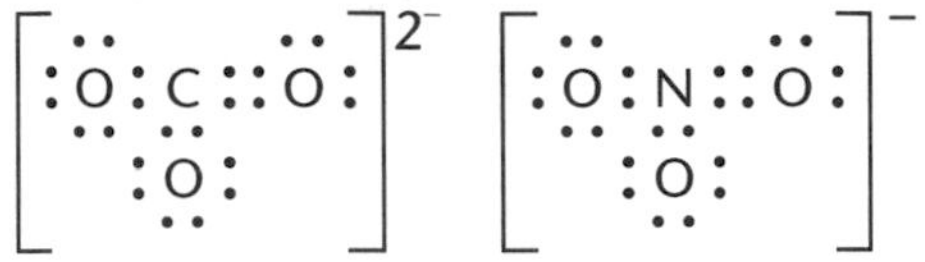

$$\left[:O:C::O: \atop :O:\right]^{2-} \quad \left[:O:N::O: \atop :O:\right]^{-}$$

3.16 Chlorate ion, ClO_3^-

$$\left[:O:Cl:O: \atop :O:\right]^{-}$$

Chapter Review

Page 149

1. (3)	2. (3)	3. (4)	4. (1)
5. (4)	6. (2)	7. (4)	8. (2)
9. (1)	10. (2)	11. (4)	12. (3)
13. (4)	14. (4)	15. (2)	16. (1)
17. (1)	18. (4)	19. (2)	20. (2)
21. (4)	22. (2)	23. (4)	24. (4)
25. (1)	26. (4)	27. (1)	28. (2)
29. (2)	30. (2)	31. (4)	32. (3)
33. (1)	34. (3)	35. (5)	

Constructed Response

Page 152

1. (a) Mg is a metallic solid with mobile electrons, MgO is ionic with no free electrons.
(b) Salt is an ionic compound, when melted the ions are released from the crystal lattice and can conduct electricity. Sugar is a covalent compound. When melted it produces molecules that do not conduct electricity.
(c) Iodine has greater dispersion forces to hold molecules in solid form.
(d) Hydrogen bonds in water hold the molecules together and give water a higher boiling point than hydrogen sulfide.

2. It is a dipole. It is tetrahedral.

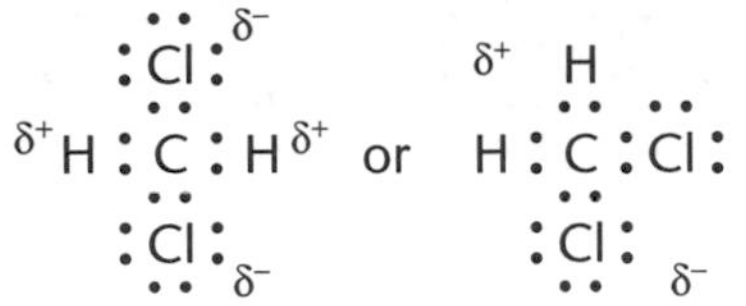

$$\delta^+ H:C:H\,\delta^+ \quad or \quad H:C:Cl:$$

Chemistry Challenge

Page 153

1. c
2. a
3. b
4. d
5. a
6. a
7. c
8. d
9. a
10. e

CHAPTER 4

Practice

Page 159

4.1 (a) BaO, barium oxide
(b) CaI_2, calcium iodide
(c) Al_2S_3, aluminum sulfide
(d) Na_3N, sodium nitride
(e) K_2S, potassium sulfide

Page 160

4.2 (a) Fe_2O_3, iron(III) oxide
(b) $CoCl_2$, cobalt(II) chloride
(c) PbS_2, lead(IV) sulfide
(d) NiO, nickel(II) oxide

Page 161

4.3 (a) $AlPO_4$, aluminum phosphate
(b) Na_2CO_3, sodium carbonate
(c) $Ba(NO_3)_2$, barium nitrate
(d) $Ni(OH)_3$, nickel(III) hydroxide
(e) $(NH_4)_2SO_4$, ammonium sulfate

4.4 (a) barium phosphate, $Ba_3(PO_4)_2$
(b) calcium hydroxide, $Ca(OH)_2$
(c) ammonium chloride, NH_4Cl
(d) sodium sulfide, Na_2S
(e) sodium sulfite, Na_2SO_3
(f) sodium sulfate, Na_2SO_4
(g) iron(II) sulfate, $FeSO_4$

Page 163

4.5 (a) $SiBr_4$, silicon tetrabromide
(b) N_2O, dinitrogen monoxide
(c) CS_2, carbon disulfide
(d) PCl_3, phosphorus trichloride

Page 165

4.6 (a) +7
(b) +4
(c) +2
(d) +3

4.7 (a) +3
(b) +5
(c) +7
(d) +6

Page 166

4.8 (a) nitrogen monoxide, NO
(b) dinitrogen trioxide, N_2O_3
(c) iron(III) oxide, Fe_2O_3
(d) carbon monoxide, CO
(e) nickel(II) oxide, NiO
(f) zinc chloride, $ZnCl_2$
(g) sulfur dichloride, SCl_2

Page 169

4.9 (a) NH_4Cl
$$N = 1 \times 14.0 = 14.0 \text{ g}$$
$$H = 4 \times 1.0 = 4.0 \text{ g}$$
$$Cl = 1 \times 35.5 = \underline{35.5 \text{ g}}$$
$$54 \text{ g}$$

(b) $Fe_2(SO_4)_3$
$$Fe = 2 \times 56 = 112 \text{ g}$$
$$S = 3 \times 32 = 96 \text{ g}$$
$$O = 12 \times 16 = \underline{192 \text{ g}}$$
$$400. \text{ g}$$

(c) Na_2SO_4
$$Na = 2 \times 23 = 46 \text{ g}$$
$$S = 1 \times 32 = 32 \text{ g}$$
$$O = 4 \times 16 = \underline{64 \text{ g}}$$
$$142 \text{ g}$$

(d) $CaCO_3$
$$Ca = 1 \times 40 = 40 \text{ g}$$
$$C = 1 \times 12 = 12 \text{ g}$$
$$O = 3 \times 16 = \underline{48 \text{ g}}$$
$$100. \text{ g}$$

(e) $(NH_4)_2Cr_2O_7$
$$N = 2 \times 14 = 28 \text{ g}$$
$$H = 8 \times 1 = 8 \text{ g}$$
$$Cr = 2 \times 52 = 104 \text{ g}$$
$$O = 7 \times 16 = \underline{112 \text{ g}}$$
$$252 \text{ g}$$

Page 172

4.10 (a) $Zn + 2 HCl \rightarrow ZnCl_2 + H_2$
(b) $FeCl_3 + 3 NaOH \rightarrow Fe(OH)_3 + 3 NaCl$
(c) $4 HgO \rightarrow 2 Hg_2O + O_2$
(d) $2 Ag + S \rightarrow Ag_2S$
(e) $3 Cl_2 + 2 AlBr3 \rightarrow 3 Br_2 + 2 AlCl_3$

Page 175

4.11 (a) single replacement
(b) double replacement
(c) decomposition, or analysis
(d) combination
(e) single replacement

Page 176

4.12 (a) $Mg + NiCl_2 \rightarrow MgCl_2 + Ni$
(b) $Al + 3 AgNO_3 \rightarrow Al(NO_3)_3 + 3 Ag$
(c) $FeCl_3 + 3 AgNO_3 \rightarrow 3 AgCl + Fe(NO_3)_3$
(d) $H_2 + CuO \rightarrow H_2O + Cu$
(e) $3 Ba(OH)_2 + Fe_2(SO_4)_3 \rightarrow 3 BaSO_4 + 2 Fe(OH)_3$

Chapter Review

Page 177

1. (3)   2. (1)   3. (3)   4. (2)
5. (4)   6. (2)   7. (3)   8. (2)
9. (3)   10. (2)   11. (2)   12. (3)
13. (2)   14. (4)   15. (1)

Constructed Response

Page 178

1. $Ca + 2 H_2O \rightarrow Ca(OH)_2 + H_2$ The total mass of the reactants = the total mass of the products, 76.

2. (a) the carbon is +4, the nitrogen +5, the sulfur +6, and the phosphorous +5.

   (b) In each case, the maximum oxidation state = the number of valence electrons.

   (c) +7

   (d) ClO_4^-

CHAPTER 5

Practice

Page 190

5.1 (a) increases
    (b) increases
    (c) decreases

5.2 (a) remains the same
    (b) decreases
    (c) increases

5.3 (a) Be
    (b) Cl
    (c) K

Chapter Review

Page 196

1. (1)   2. (1)   3. (4)   4. (4)
5. (2)   6. (3)   7. (4)   8. (3)
9. (1)   10. (4)   11. (2)   12. (4)
13. (2)   14. (4)   15. (3)   16. (1)
17. (3)   18. (3)   19. (4)   20. (3)
21. (3)   22. (2)   23. (4)   24. (4)
25. (4)   26. (3)   27. (1)   28. (3)
29. (2)

Constructed Response

Page 198

1. The atomic radius of element 104 (Rf) should be about 174 picometers. Its radius would be slightly larger than Hf (167 picometers), the element immediately above it.

2. Because At falls between Po (812 kJ/mole) and Rn (1037 kJ/mole), one possible ionization energy is 900 kJ/mole. (Answers should be between 812 kJ/mole and 1037 kJ/mole.)

3. The color changes indicate that X is most likely a transition element. A transition element that has a greater atomic mass than the elements on either side of it would be Co.

4. There are 32 elements in Period 6.

CHAPTER 6

Practice

Page 205

6.1 $2 K + 2 H_2O \rightarrow 2 KOH + H_2$

6.2 $2 H_2 + O_2 \rightarrow 2 H_2O$

6.3 (a) (1) single replacement
(6) exothermic

(b) (4) combination
(6) exothermic

6.4 Sodium because the light is yellow-orange, the color of the sodium flame.

6.5 The reaction between Na and HCL and K and HCl are too violent.

Page 211

6.6 Ca^{2+} and Mg^{2+}

6.7 (a) Element X has a lower ionization energy than element Y.

(b) Element X has a lower electronegativity than element Y.

(c) Atomic radius of X is larger than Y's.

(d) X's ion is larger than Y's.

(e) Element X forms a 1+ ion, while element Y forms a 2+ ion.

(f) Element X is more active than element Y.

6.8 The alkali metals and alkaline earth metals are too reactive to remain uncombined.

6.9 $Ba + 2 H_2O \rightarrow Ba(OH)_2 + H_2$
Ba is faster than Ca, because Ba is more active.

Page 219

6.10 The Group 13 elements have 3 electrons in their outer shell that they can lose to form 3+ ions. Boron does not form 3+ ions because it has a small radius and higher ionization energy than the other Group 13 elements.

6.11 Tin and lead have much larger atomic radii and much smaller ionization energies than do carbon, so they are able to lose electrons in reactions and act as metals.

6.12 The nitrogen molecule contains a triple bond, which is difficult to break. This prevents nitrogen from reacting readily with other elements.

6.13 The Group 15 elements each have 5 electrons in their outer energy level that can be lost.

Page 231

6.14 oxygen

6.15 radon

6.16 Hydrogen can react explosively with the oxygen in the air. Helium is used because it is safer.

6.17 O_2 and O_3

Chapter Review

Page 231

1. (1)	2. (1)	3. (2)	4. (4)
5. (2)	6. (2)	7. (2)	8. (4)
9. (2)	10. (3)	11. (3)	12. (2)
13. (3)	14. (1)	15. (2)	16. (2)
17. (1)	18. (1)	19. (1)	20. (2)
21. (1)	22. (2)	23. (3)	24. (1)
25. (4)			

Constructed Response

Page 234

1. (a) Ca
   (b) Kr
   (c) Bi
   (d) N
   (e) F
   (f) N
   (g) S

2. SO_2 in the air reacts with water and oxygen in the air to form sulfuric acid. The acid dissolves in raindrops forming acid rain.

3. The burning of fossil fuels produces CO_2 gas. CO_2 in the atmosphere traps heat, so that increased quantities of CO_2 may be causing global warming.

4. Perform a flame test on both solutions. The KBr would produce a violet flame while the NaBr would produce a yellow-orange flame.

CHAPTER 7

Practice

Page 239

7.1 (a) 20. grams of NaOH
(b) 450 grams of $CaCO_3$
(c) 65 grams of $Ba(NO_3)_2$
(d) 186 grams of Na_2O

7.2 (a) 1.5 mol NaOH
(b) 0.75 mol $CaCO_3$
(c) 0.100 mol $Ba(NO_3)_2$
(d) 5.0 mol Na_2O

7.3 120g/mol is the molar mass of the substance.

Page 243

7.4 molar mass CO = 12 + 16 = 28 g/mole

$$\%C = \frac{12\ g}{28\ g} \times 100\% = 43\%\ C$$

$$\%O = \frac{16\ g}{28\ g} \times 100\% = 57\%\ O$$

(b) molar mass $ZnSiO_3$ = 65 + 28 + 3(16) = 141 g/mole

$$\%Zn = \frac{65\ g}{141\ g} \times 100\% = 46\%\ Zn$$

$$\%Si = \frac{28\ g}{141\ g} \times 100\% = 20\%\ Si$$

$$\%O = \frac{48\ g}{141\ g} \times 100\% = 34\%\ O$$

(c) molar mass H_3PO_4 = 3(1) + 31 + 4(16) = 98 g/mole

$$\%H = \frac{3\ g}{98\ g} \times 100\% = 3\%\ H$$

$$\%P = \frac{31\ g}{98\ g} \times 100\% = 32\%\ P$$

$$\%O = \frac{64\ g}{98\ g} \times 100\% = 65\%\ O$$

(d) molar mass $Ca(NO_3)_2$ = $(1 \times 40) + (2 \times 14) + (6 \times 16)$ = 164 g/mole

$$\%Ca = \frac{40\ g}{164\ g} \times 100\% = 24\%\ Ca$$

$$\%\ N = \frac{28\ g}{164\ g} \times 100\% = 17\%\ N$$

$$\%O = \frac{96\ g}{164\ g} \times 100\% = 59\%\ O$$

7.5 molar mass $Ba(OH)_2 \bullet 8\ H_2O$ = 137 + 2(16 + 1) + 8[2(1) + 16] = 315 g/mole

mass H_2O = 8[2(1) + 16] = 144 g

$$\%H_2O = \frac{144\ g}{315\ g} \times 100\% =$$
45.7% H_2O = 46% water

Page 244

7.6 (a) HO—ratio is 1:1
(b) C_7H_{12}—ratio is 7:12
(c) CH—ratio is 1:1

Page 247

7.7 (a) C = 75 g ÷ 12 g/mole = 6.25 moles; mole ratio is 6.25/6.25 = 1

H = 25 g ÷ 1 g/mole = 25 moles; mole ratio is 25/6.25 = 4

empirical formula = CH_4

(b) Ca = 40 g ÷ 40 g/mole = 1 mole; mole ratio is 1/1 = 1

C = 12 g ÷ 12 g/mole = 1 mole; mole ratio is 1/1 = 1

O = 48 g ÷ 16 g/mole = 3 moles; mole ratio is 3/1 = 3

empirical formula = $CaCO_3$

(c) $H = 2.5$ g $\div$ 1 g/mole = 2.5 moles; mole ratio is $2.5/2.5 = 1$

$Na = 57.5$ g $\div$ 23 g/mole = 2.5 moles; mole ratio is $2.5/2.5 = 1$

$O = 40$ g $\div$ 16 g/mole = 2.5 moles; mole ratio is $2.5/2.5 = 1$

empirical formula = NaOH

(d) $C = 40.0$ g $\div$ 12 g/mole = 3.33 moles; mole ratio is $3.33/3.33 = 1$

$H = 6.7$ g $\div$ 1 g/mole = 6.7 moles; mole ratio is $6.7/3.33 = 2$

$O = 53.3$ g $\div$ 16 g/mole = 3.33 moles; mole ratio is $3.33/3.33 = 1$

empirical formula = CH_2O

(e) $Ca = 66.0$ g $\div$ 40.0 g/mole = 1.65 moles; mole ratio is $1.65/1.1 = 1.5$

$P = 34.0$ g $\div$ 30.9 g/mole = 1.1 moles; mole ratio is $1.1/1.1 = 1$

empirical formula = $Ca_{1.5}P_1 = Ca_3P_2$

(f) $A1 = 8.3$ g $\div$ 27 g/mole = 0.31 mole; mole ratio is $0.31/0.31 = 1$

$C1 = 32.7$ g $\div$ 35.5 g/mole = 0.92 mole; mole ratio is $0.92/0.31 = 2.97 \approx 3$

$O = 59.0$ g $\div$ 16 g/mole = 3.69 moles; mole ratio is $3.69/0.31 = 11.9 \approx 12$

empirical formula = $AlCl_3O_{12}$ or $Al(ClO_4)_3$

7.8 (a) $Ca = 1.8$g $\div$ 40 g/mole = 0.045 mole; mole ratio is $0.045/0.045 = 1$

$Cl = 3.2$ g $\div$ 35.5 g/mole = 0.090 mole; mole ratio is $0.090/0.045 = 2$

empirical formula = $CaCl_2$

(b) $Cs = 8.8$ g $\div$ 133 g/mole = 0.066 mole; mole ratio is $0.066/0.066 = 1$

$Cl = 2.35$ g $\div$ 35.5 g/mole = 0.066 mole; mole ratio is $0.066/0.066 = 1$

empirical formula = CsCl

(c) $Al = 233.7$ g $\div$ 27 g/mole = 8.7 moles; mole ratio is $8.7/8.7 = 1$

$S = 416$ g $\div$ 32 g/mole = 13.0 moles; mole ratio is $13.0/8.7 = 1.49 = 1.5$

$AlS_{1.5}$ or Al_2S_3

(d) $Ni = 10.26$ g $\div$ 57 g/mole = 0.18 mole; mole ratio is $0.18/0.18 = 1$

$N = 4.90$ g $\div$ 14 g/mole = 0.35 mole; mole ratio is $0.35/0.18 = 1.9 = 2$

$O = 16.8$ g $\div$ 16 g/mole = 1.05 moles; mole ratio is $1.05/0.18 = 5.83 = 6$

empirical formula = NiN_2O_6 or $Ni(NO_3)_2$

Page 249

7.9 Mass of empirical formula $CH = 12 + 1 = 13$ g

Molecular mass $\div$ mass of empirical formula 78 g $\div$ 13 g = 6

Molecular formula $(CH)_6$ or C_6H_6 is the formula of benzene.

7.10 $C = 85.7$ g $\div$ 12 g/mole = 7.14 moles; mole ratio is $7.14/7.14 = 1$

$H = 14.3$ g $\div$ 1 g/mole = 14.3 moles; mole ratio is $14.3/7.14 = 2$

empirical formula is CH_2

mass of empirical formula = $12 + 2 = 14$

70 g/14 g = 5

formula = $(CH_2)_5 = C_5H_{10}$

7.11 C_2H_5 mass of empirical formula
= 2(12) + 5(1) = 29 g
58 g/29 g = 2
formula = $(C_2H_5)_2$ = C_4H_{10} is
butane.

7.12 C = 60.0 g ÷ 12 g/mole =
5 moles; mole ratio is 5/2.2 =
2.3; 2.3 × 4 = 9.2 = 9
H = 4.48 g ÷ 1 g/mole = 4.48
moles; mole ratio is 4.48/2.2 =
2.0; 2.0 × 4 = 8
O = 35.5 ÷ 16 g/mole =
2.2 moles; mole ratio is 2.2/2.2
= 1.0; 1.0 × 4 = 4
empiricial formula is $C_9H_8O_4$
mass of empirical formula =
9(12) + 8(1) + 4(6) = 180
180 g/180 g = 1
molecular formular = $C_9H_8O_4$

Page 252

7.13 (a) $\dfrac{x \text{ moles He}}{3} = \dfrac{6 \text{ moles NH}_3}{2}$,
x = 9 moles of hydrogen
(9 moles H_2)

(b) $\dfrac{x \text{ moles N}_2}{1} = \dfrac{0.60 \text{ mole H}}{3}$,
0.20 mole of nitrogen
(0.20 mole N_2)

(c) $\dfrac{x \text{ moles NH}_3}{2} = \dfrac{0.5 \text{ mole N}_2}{1}$,
1.0 mole of ammonia
(1 mole NH_3)

7.14 (a) 4.6 moles $Pb(CH_3)_4$ ×
$\dfrac{15 \text{ moles O}_2}{2 \text{ moles Pb(CH}_3)_4}$ =
34.5 moles of O_2

(b) 5 moles $PB(CH_3)_4$ ×
$\dfrac{8 \text{ moles CO}_2}{2 \text{ moles Pb(CH}_3)_4}$ =
20 moles of CO_2

(c) 7.5 moles O_2 ×
$\dfrac{12 \text{ moles H}_2O}{15 \text{ moles O}_2}$ =
6 moles of H_2O

7.15 When 9 moles of CO_2 form, 12
moles of H_2O form.
Propane + O_2 → $3CO_2$ + 4 H_2O
The coefficient in front of the
H_2O is 4.

Page 258

7.16 (a) molar mass H_2O = 2(1) + 16
= 18 g/mole
36 g H_2O ÷ 18 g/mole =
2.0 mole H_2O

(b) molar mass NaOH =
23 + 16 + 1 = 40 g/mole
6.0 g NaOH ÷ 40 g/mole =
0.15 mole NaOH

(c) molar mass $CaCO_3$ =
40 + 12 + 3(16) =100 g/mole
40 g $CaCO_3$ ÷ 100 g/mole =
0.4 mole $CaCO_3$

(d) 44.8 L CO_2 ÷ 22.4 L/mole =
2 moles CO_2

(e) 11.2 L He ÷ 22.4 L/mole =
0.5 mole He

(f) 56 L O_2 ÷ 22.4 L/mole =
2.5 moles O_2

7.17 (a) molar mass H_2O = 2(1) + 16
= 18 g/mole
1.5 moles H_2O × 18 g/mole
= 27 g H_2O

(b) molar mass N_2 = 2(14) =
28 g/mole
0.30 mole N_2 × 28 g/mole =
8.4 g N_2

(c) molar mass NO_2 = 14 + 2(16)
= 46 g/mole
0.40 mole NO_2 × 46 g/mole
= 18 g NO_2

(d) 44.8 L H_2 ÷ 22.4 L/mole =
2.00 moles H_2
2.00 moles H_2 × 2 g/mole =
4 g H_2

(e) 56 L Ne ÷ 22.4 L mole =
2.5 moles Ne
2.5 moles Ne × 20 g/mole =
50 g Ne

(f) 5.6 L $O_2 \div 22.4$ L/mole =
0.25 mole O_2

0.25 mole $O_2 \times 32$ g/mole =
8.0 g O_2

7.18 (a) 3.0 moles Ar $\times 22.4$ L/mole
$= 67.2$ L Ar

(b) 0.40 mole $CO_2 \times 22.4$
L/mole $= 9.0$ L CO_2

(c) 1.5 moles $Cl_2 \times 22.4$ L/mole
$= 34$ L Cl_2

(d) molar mass He $= 4.00$ g

16 g He $\div 4.00$ g/mole =
4.00 moles He

4.00 moles He $\times 22.4$
L/mole $= 89.6$ L He

(e) molar mass $O_2 = 2(16) =$
32 g/mole

16 g $O_2 \div 32$ g/mole =
0.50 mole O_2

0.50 mole $O_2 \times 22.4$ L/mole
$= 11$ L O_2

(f) molar mass $N_2O = 2(14) +$
$16 = 44$ g/mole

4.4 g $N_2O \div 44$ g/mole =
0.10 mole N_2O

0.10 mole $N_2O \times 22.4$
L/mole $= 2.2$ L N_2O

Page 259

7.19 D = *molar mass* $\div 22.4$ L/mole

(a) molar mass CO $= 12 + 16 =$
28 g/mole

28 g/mole $\div 22.4$ L/mole =
1.3 g/L

(b) molar mass $O_2 = 2(16) =$
32 g/mole

32 g/mole $\div 22.4$ L/mole =
1.4 g/L

(c) molar mass Ar $= 39.9$ g/mole

39.9 g/mole $\div 22.4$ L/mole
$= 1.78$ g/L

(d) molar mass $NH_3 = 14 + 3(1)$
$= 17$ g/mole

g/mole $\div 22.4$ L/mole =
0.76 g/L

7.20 D $\times 22.4$ L/ mole = *molar mass*
1.98 g/L $\times 22.4$ L/mole =
44.4 g/mole

7.21 D = mass $\div$ volume
D $= 11.4$ g $\div 4.00$ L $= 2.85$ g/L
D = *molar mass* $\div 22.4$ L/mole
2.85 g/L = $x \div 22.4$ L/mole
$x = 63.8$ g/mole

Page 262

7.22 23 g $C_2H_5OH \div 46$ g/mole =
0.5 mole C_2H_5OH

0.5 mole $C_2H_5OH \times$

$\dfrac{2 \text{ moles } CO_2}{1 \text{ mole } C_2H_3OH} = 1$ mole CO_2

1 mole $CO_2 \times 44$ g/mole =
44 g CO_2

7.23 20 g NaOH $\div 40$ g/mole =
0.5 mole NaOH

0.5 mole NaHO $\times$

$\dfrac{1 \text{ mole } Na_2O}{2 \text{ moles NaOH}} =$
0.25 mole Na_2O

7.24 0.5 mole $NH_3 \times$

$\dfrac{3 \text{ moles } H_2}{2 \text{ moles } NH_3} \times \dfrac{2 \text{ g } H_2}{1 \text{ mole } H_2} =$
1.5 g H_2

Page 264

7.25 $2 H_2O_2 \rightarrow O_2 + 2 H_2O$

6.8 g $H_2O_2 \div 34$ g/mole =
0.20 mole H_2O_2

0.20 mole $H_2O_2 \times \dfrac{1 \text{ mole } O_2}{2 \text{ moles } H_2O_2} =$

0.10 mole O_2

0.10 mole $O_2 \times 22.4$ L/mole =
2.24 L O_2

7.26 13.44 L $H_2 \div 22.4$ L/mole =
0.600 mole H_2

0.600 mole $H_2 \times \dfrac{2 \text{ moles Al}}{3 \text{ moles } H_2} =$
0.400 mole Al

0.400 mole Al $\times 27$ g/mole =
11 g Al

7.27 $\dfrac{11.2 \text{ L N}_2}{1} = \dfrac{x \text{ L H}_2}{3}$, $x = 33.6 \text{ L H}_2$

Page 267

7.28 $30 \text{ L N}_2 \times \dfrac{3 \text{ moles H}_2}{1 \text{ mole N}_2} = 90 \text{ L of H}_2$

7.29 (a) $\dfrac{24 \text{ L SO}_3}{8} = \dfrac{x}{12} = 36 \text{ L O}_2$

(b) $89.6 \text{ L SO}_3 \times \dfrac{1 \text{ mole SO}_3}{22.4 \text{ L SO}_3} \times$

$\dfrac{1 \text{ mole S}_8}{8 \text{ moles SO}_3} = 0.500 \text{ mole S}_8$

(c) The method used in part (a) only applies to gases, S_8 is a solid.

Page 271

7.30 (a) $16 \text{ g O}_2 \div 32 \text{ g/mole} = 0.5 \text{ mole O}_2$

$0.5 \text{ mole O}_2 \times \dfrac{6 \text{ moles H}_2\text{O}}{7 \text{ moles O}_2} = 0.43 \text{ mole H}_2\text{O}$

$9 \text{ g C}_2\text{H}_6 \div 30 \text{ g/mole} = 0.3 \text{ mole C}_2\text{H}_6$

$0.3 \text{ mole C}_2\text{H}_6 \times \dfrac{6 \text{ moles H}_2\text{O}}{2 \text{ moles C}_2\text{H}_6} = 0.9 \text{ mole H}_2\text{O}$

limiting reagent is O_2

$0.43 \text{ mole H}_2\text{O} \times 18 \text{ g/mole} = 7.7 \text{ g H}_2\text{O}$

(b)

Moles	$2 \text{ C}_2\text{H}_6$ +	$7 \text{ O}_2 \rightarrow$	4 CO_2 +	$5 \text{ H}_2\text{O}$
Init.	0.3 mole	0.5 mole	0	0
Change	–0.14	–0.5	+0.29	+0.43
Final	0.16	0	0.29	0.43

$0.43 \text{ mole H}_2\text{O} \times \dfrac{2 \text{ moles C}_2\text{H}_6}{6 \text{ moles H}_2\text{O}} = 0.143 \text{ mole C}_2\text{H}_6$

$0.5 \text{ mole O}_2 \times \dfrac{4 \text{ moles CO}_2}{7 \text{ moles O}_2} = 0.286 \text{ mole CO}_2$

excess ethane = 0.16 mole

Page 272

7.31 $34 \text{ g H}_2\text{O}_2 \div 34 \text{ g/mole} = 1 \text{ mole H}_2\text{O}_2$

$1 \text{ mole H}_2\text{O}_2 \times \dfrac{1 \text{ mole O}_2}{2 \text{ moles H}_2\text{O}_2} = 0.5 \text{ mole O}_2$

theoretical yield: $0.5 \text{ mole O}_2 \times 32 \text{ g/mole} = 16 \text{ g O}_2$

$\dfrac{12 \text{ g O}_2}{16 \text{ g O}_2} \times 100\% = 75\% \text{ yield}$

Page 275

7.32 (a) $2\text{H}_2\text{O}_2 \rightarrow \text{O}_2 + 2 \text{ H}_2\text{O}$

$\text{g H}_2\text{O}_2 \div 34 \text{ g/mole} = 1.0 \text{ mole H}_2\text{O}_2$

$1.0 \text{ mole H}_2\text{O}_2 \times \dfrac{1 \text{ mole O}_2}{2 \text{ moles H}_2\text{O}_2} = 0.5 \text{ mole O}_2$

$0.50 \text{ mole O}_2 \times 22.4 \text{ L/mole} = 11.2 \text{ L O}_2 \text{ at STP}$

$V_1/T_1 = V_2/T_2$

$11.2 \text{ L}/273 \text{ K} = V_2/298 \text{ K}$

$V_2 = 12.2 \text{ L}$

(b) $0.5 \text{ mole O}_2 = 16 \text{ grams}$, the mass does not change with change in temperature.

Page 276

7.33 $2 \text{ C}_8\text{H}_{18} + 25 \text{ O}_2 \rightarrow 16 \text{ CO}_2 + 18 \text{ H}_2\text{O}$

$11.2 \text{ L C}_8\text{H}_{18} \times \dfrac{25 \text{ moles O}_2}{2 \text{ moles C}_8\text{H}_{18}} = 140 \text{ L O}_2$

$140 \text{ L O}_2 \times \dfrac{5 \text{ L air}}{1 \text{ L O}_2} = 700 \text{ L air}$

Page 277

7.34 $\dfrac{R_1}{R_2} = \sqrt{\dfrac{M_2}{M_1}}$

$\dfrac{R_1}{R_2} = \sqrt{\dfrac{84}{20}}$

$\dfrac{R_1}{R_2} = 2.0$

Chapter Review

Page 277

1. (1) 2.16 g Ag $\div$ 108 g/mole =
   $0.02 = 2 \times 10^{-2}$

2. (2) CuO = $64 + 16 = 80$ g/mole
   $\dfrac{16\text{ g}}{80\text{ g}} \times 100\% = 20\%$

3. (2) $H_3PO_4 = 3(1) + 31 + 4(16) = 98$
   g/mole; $\dfrac{3}{98} \times 100$

4. (1) %Ca = $\dfrac{40}{200} \times 100\% = 20\%$
   %Br = $\dfrac{160}{200} \times 100\% = 80\%$

5. (2) S = 50 g $\div$ 32 g/mole =
   1.56 moles; mole ratio is
   $1.56/1.56 = 1$
   O = 50 g $\div$ 16 g/mole =
   3.12 moles; mole ratio is
   $3.12/1.56 = 2$
   empirical formula is SO_2

6. (3) All three are binary compounds.
   Mg has the smallest atomic
   mass, therefore, oxygen makes
   up the greatest percentage.

7. (3) 1 mole $N_2 \times \dfrac{2\text{ moles }NH_3}{1\text{ mole }N_2} =$
   2 moles NH_3

8. (3) $2(CH_2) = C_2H_4$

9. (4) 3 moles Cu $\times \dfrac{4\text{ moles }HNO_3}{1\text{ mole Cu}} =$
   12 moles HNO_3

10. (3)

11. (2) 0.050 mole $Al_2(SO_4)_3 \times$
    $\dfrac{3\text{ moles }PbSO_4}{1\text{ mole }Al_2(SO_4)_3} =$
    0.15 mole $Al_2(SO_4)_3$

12. (2) $40.$ g NaOH = 1 mole
    24 g H_2O = 1.3 moles
    200 g PbS = 0.8 mole
    $250.$ g $PbSO_4$ = 0.8 mole

13. (1) $CaCO_3 = (1 \times 40) + (1 \times 12)$
    $+ (3 \times 16) = 100$ g/mole
    $\dfrac{20\text{ g}}{100\text{ g/mole}} = 0.2$ mole

14. (1) 4 moles $H_2O \times \dfrac{1\text{ mole }O_2}{2\text{ moles }H_2O} =$
    2 moles O_2

15. (4) 90 g $H_2O \div 18$ g/mole =
    5 moles H_2O
    5 moles $H_2O \times \dfrac{2\text{ moles }H_2}{2\text{ moles }H_2O} =$
    5 moles H_2
    5 moles $H_2 \times 22.4$ L/mole =
    112 L H_2

16. (4) 1 mole $KMnO_4 \times$
    $\dfrac{8\text{ moles }H_2O}{2\text{ }KMnO_4} = 4$ moles H_2O

17. (3) 1 mole $KMnO_4 \times$
    $\dfrac{2\text{ moles }KCl}{2\text{ moles }KMnO_4} = 1$ mole KCl
    1 mole KCl $\times 74$ g/mole =
    74 g KCl

18. (3) 1 mole $KMnO_4 \times$
    $\dfrac{5\text{ moles }Cl_2}{2\text{ moles }KMnO_4} =$
    2.5 moles Cl_2
    2.5 moles $Cl_2 \times 22.4$ L/mole =
    56 L Cl_2

19. (2) 0.500 mole $\times 22.4$ L/mole =
    11.2 L

20. (3) 3.01×10^{23} molecules $\div 6.02$
    $\times 10^{23}$ molecules/mole =
    0.5 mole
    0.5 mole $\times 22.4$ L/mole =
    11.2 L

21. (3) 3 L $NH_3 \times \dfrac{3\text{ moles }H_2}{2\text{ moles }NH_3} =$
    4.5 L H_2

22. (4) 56 g $N_2 \div 28$ g/mole =
    2 moles N_2
    2 moles $N_2 \times 22.4$ L/mole =
    44.8 L

23. (2) 150 L $O_2 \times \dfrac{3\text{ moles }CO_2}{5\text{ moles }O_3} =$
    90 L CO_2

24. (3) 5.6 L $\div 22.4$ L/mole =
    0.25 mole
    11 g = 0.25 mole
    1 mole = 11 g $\times 4 = 44$ g

25. (4) At STP, 1 mole of gas occupies 22.4 L, therefore, 28 g = 1 mole.

26. (3) 22.4 L O_2 at STP = 1 mole = 32 g O_2

27. (1) 14 g occupy 11.2 L, therefore, 28 g will occupy 22.4 L.
1 mole = 28 g
$CO = 12 + 16 = 28$ g/mole

28. (4) 71 g $Cl_2 \div 22.4$ L = 3 g/L

29. (3) 22.4 L HI $\times \dfrac{1 \text{ mole } H_2}{2 \text{ moles HI}} =$ 11.2 L H_2

30. (2) 2 g He $\div$ 4 g/mole = 0.5 mole He
0.5 mole He $\times$ 22.4 L/mole = 11.2 L

31. (3) 9.03×10^{23} molecules $\div 6.02 \times 10^{23}$ molecules/mole = 1.5 mole
1.5 mole $\times$ 22.4 L/mole = 33.6 L

32. (2) $NO_2 = 14 + 2(16) =$ 46 g/mole $\div$ 22.4 L/mole = 2.05 g/L
$NO = 14 + 16 = 30$ g/mole $\div$ 22.4 L/mole = 1.34 g/L
$N_2 = 2(14) = 28 \div 22.4$ L/mole = 1.25 g/L
$H_2 = 2(1) \div 22.4$ L/mole = 0.089 g/L

33. (4) 6.02×10^{23} molecules = 1 mole N_2
From the balanced equation, 1 mole $N_2 \rightarrow$ 2 moles NH_3
2 moles $\times 6.02 \times 10^{23}$ molecules/mole = 12.04×10^{23} molecules

34. (1)

35. (1) $2 H_2O \rightarrow 2 H_2 + O_2$
1 mole $H_2O \rightarrow$ 1 mole $H_2 +$ 0.5 mole O_2
1 mole $H_2 = 22.4$ L H_2;
0.5 mole $O_2 = 11.2$ L O_2

36. (4) 1.00 g/L $\times$ 22.4 L/mole = 22.4 g

37. (3)

38. (3) $H_2O = 2(1) + 16 = 18$ g/mole;
60 g $-$ 18 g = 42 g

Chemistry Challenge

Page 280

1. (d)
2. (c)
3. (e)
4. (b)
5. (a)
6. (e)
7. (b)
8. (d)
9. (e)
10. (d)

CHAPTER 8

Practice

Page 288

8.1 (a) Iodine and CCl_4 are both nonpolar molecules.
(b) Iodine is more soluble in CCl_4 than in H_2O.
(c) Water and CCl_4 are immiscible.
(d) Water is less dense than CCl_4.
(e) Benzene layer with iodine, the purple layer, would be above the water, because benzene is less dense than water.

Page 289

8.2 (a) 4 water and gasoline are immiscible liquids
(b) 3 benzene and carbon tetrachloride are miscible liquids
(c) 1 the sulfur and water contains an insoluble solid

8.3 (a) 1, HCl gas is more soluble in water, because HCl is polar, as is water.

(b) 2, Br_2 is more soluble in carbon tetrachloride, because Br_2 and CCl_4 are both nonpolar.
(c) 1, $NiNO_3$ is more soluble in water, because $NiNO_3$ is ionic, and will dissolve only in a highly polar solvent like water.

Page 292

8.4 (a) Supersaturated, because a large number of crystals formed when just one was added.
(b) Dissolving is endothermic because heat was released on recrystallization.

Page 293

8.5 24°C

8.6 unsaturated

8.7 23 g

8.8 10 g NaCl

8.9 (a) Water evaporated, and the solution became more concentrated. When it passed the saturation point, crystals formed.
(b) 89 grams of water remained.

Page 296

8.10 An increase in temperature usually increases the solubility of solids in liquids.

8.11 An increase in temperature usually decreases the solubility of gases in liquids.

8.12 The solubility of the carbon dioxide would increase. Decreasing the volume of the container increases the pressure of the gas (Boyle's Law), and gases are more soluble at high pressures.

8.13 The air pressure deep in the mine was greater than the pressure at the surface. The decrease in pressure as the miner was brought up decreased the solubility of the nitrogen gas.

Page 299

8.14 (a) $ppm = \dfrac{g\ solute}{g\ solution} \times$ 1,000,000

$$\dfrac{0.0040\ g\ NaCl}{1000.\ solution} \times 1,000,000 =$$

4 ppm

(b) $ppm = \dfrac{g\ solute}{g\ solution} \times 1,000,000$

$$\dfrac{0.035\ g\ Na}{250\ g\ soda} \times 1,000,000 =$$

140 ppm

8.15 $\% = \dfrac{g\ solute}{g\ solution} \times 100$

$$\dfrac{27\ g\ sugar}{250\ g\ soda} \times 100 = 11\%$$

8.16 40 ppm $= x$ grams $\times$ 1,000,000/250g
$x = 0.010$ grams

Page 302

8.17 (a) *Molarity = moles* $\div$ L
$x = 2$ moles $\div$ 0.5 L = 4 M

(b) moles NaOH = 20.0 g NaOH $\div$ 40.0 g/mole = 0.500 mole
$x = 0.500$ mole $\div$ 2.0 L = 0.25 M

(c) mole C_2H_5OH = 23 g C_2H_5OH $\div$ 46 g/mole = 0.50 mole

$x = 0.50$ mole $\div$ 0.5 L = 1 M

8.18 (a) *Molarity* $\times$ L = *moles*

2.00 M $\times$ 4.00 L = 8.00 moles HNO_3

8.00 moles $\times$ 63.0 g/mole = 504 g HNO_3

(b) 4.00 M $\times$ 0.200 L = 0.800 mole glucose

0.800 mole $\times$ 180 g/mole = 144 g glucose

8.19 moles Na_2CO_3 = 10.6 g $\div$ 106 g/mole = 0.100 mole

0.100 mole Na_2CO_3 $\div$ 0.0500 L = 2 M Na_2CO_3

2 M Na_2CO_3 $\times$ 2 Na^+/mole = 4 M

Page 304

8.20 $M_0 \times V_0 = M_f \times V_f$

$6.0\ M \times 40.\ \text{mL} = 0.50\ M \times V_f$

$V_f = 480\ \text{mL}$

8.21 $M_0 \times V_0 = M_f \times V_f$

$4.0\ M \times 50.\ \text{mL} = M_f \times 200.\ \text{mL}$

$M_f = 1.0\ M$

8.22 $2.0\ M \times 0.0500\ \text{L} = 0.10\ \text{mole}$

$x = 0.10\ \text{mole} \div 0.50\ \text{L} = 0.20\ M$

8.23 $2.0\ M \times 0.0500\ \text{L} = 0.10\ \text{mole}$

$3.0\ M \times 0.100\ \text{L} = 0.30\ \text{mole}$

$0.10\ \text{mole} + 0.30 = 0.40\ \text{mole}$

$0.40\ \text{mole} \div 0.25\ \text{L} = 1.6\ M$

Page 306

8.24 mole sucrose $= 34.2\ \text{g} \div 342\ \text{g/mole} = 0.0100\ \text{mole}$

$0.100\ \text{mole} \div 0.250\ \text{kg} = 0.400\ m$

8.25 $300.\ \text{mL} \times 0.880\ \text{g/mL} = 264\ \text{g} = 0.264$

$0.0750\ \text{mole}\ I_2 \div 0.264\ \text{kg} = 0.284\ m$

Page 313

8.26 moles NaCl $= 5.8\ \text{g} \div 58\ \text{g/mole} = 0.10\ \text{mole}$

$m = 0.10\ \text{mole} \div 0.500\ \text{kg} = 0.20\ m$

For NaCl, $i = 2$

$\Delta t_f = 1.86°C \times m \times i$

$= 1.86 \times 0.20 \times 2$

$= -0.744°C$

The freezing point is –0.74°C.

8.27 (a) $i = 3$, $i \times m = 6$

(b) $i = 2$, $i \times m = 4$

(c) $i = 1$, $i \times m = 3$

(d) $i = 3$, $i \times m = 4.5$

c, b, d, a

Page 315

8.28 moles $H_2O = 1000.\ \text{g} \div 18\ \text{g/mole} = 56\ \text{moles}$

$X_{H_2O} = 56\ \text{moles} \div 57\ \text{moles} = 0.98$

$P_{H_2O} = P^0{}_{H_2O} \times X_{H_2O}$

$P_{H_2O} = 101.3\ \text{kPa} \times 0.98 = 99\ \text{kPa}$

$P_{H_2O} = 1\ \text{atm} \times 0.98 = 0.98\ \text{atm}$

Chapter Review

Page 316

1. (4)

2. (2)

3. (3)

4. (4)

5. (2) 4 g NaOH $\div$ 40 g/mole = 0.1 mole NaOH; 0.1 mole $\div$ 0.51 = 0.2 M

6. (4)

7. (2) $M = moles \div L$

$2\ M = x \div 0.5\ \text{L}$

$x = 1\ \text{mole}$

8. (4)

9. (2) ppm $= \dfrac{g\ \text{solute}}{g\ \text{solution}} \times 1{,}000{,}000$

$x = \dfrac{0.100\ \text{g Pb}}{2000.\ \text{g}} \times 1{,}000{,}000 = 50\ \text{ppm Pb}$

10. (2) 10 g NaOH $\div$ 40 g/mole = 0.25 mole NaOH

$M = 0.25\ \text{mole} \div 0.5\ \text{L} = 0.5\ M$

11. (3) solubility at 30°C = 48 g/100 g

solubility at 40°C = 63 g/100 g

63 g – 48 g = 15 g

12. (1)

13. (3) moles $= M \times \text{L}$

moles $= 1\ M \times 0.01\ \text{L} = 0.01\ \text{mole}$

14. (1) moles $= M \times \text{L}$

moles $= 5\ M \times 0.5\ \text{L} = 2.5\ \text{moles}$

15. (2) 20 g NaOH $\div$ 40 g/mole = 0.5 mole

0.5 mole $\div$ 0.5 L = 1 M

16. (3) $ppm = \dfrac{g \text{ solute}}{g \text{ solution}} \times$
    1,000,000

   $500 \text{ ppm} = \dfrac{0.200 \text{ g}}{x} \times$
    1,000,000

   $x = 40$

17. (1)

18. (3)

19. (2) moles $= M \times L$
    moles $= 4\,M \times 0.5 \text{ L} = 2$ moles

20. (1) 98 g $H_2SO_4 \div 98$ g/mole $=$
    1 mole
    $M = 1 \text{ mole} \div 2 \text{ L} = 0.5\,M$

21. (1) $\dfrac{10. \text{ g HCl}}{1000. \text{ g}} \times 100 = 1.0\ \%$

22. (1)

23. (4)

24. (1)

25. (4)

26. (2)

27. (3)

28. (4)

29. (3) (1) $i = 2$, (2) $i = 3$ (3) $i = 4$,
    (4) $i = 2$

30. (4) (1) $i = 2$, (2) $i = 2$, (3) $i = 2$,
    (4) $l = 3$

CHAPTER 9

Practice

Page 326

9.1 Orientation and energy of the molecules, also sufficient energy of activation.

9.2 ΔH is +. If the forward activation is greater than the reverse, the forward reaction is endothermic and has a + ΔH.

9.3 (2)

Page 332

9.4 (a) Zinc powder in hydrochloric acid would react faster, because the powder has a larger exposed surface area than the strips.
(b) Magnesium ribbon in concentrated acid is faster. Increased concentration increases reaction rates by providing a greater number of intermolecular collisions.
(c) Warm milk would get sour faster because higher temperature yields a greater number of more effective collisions.
(d) One mole iron and one mole of oxygen in the 1-liter container. The smaller volume increases the frequency of collisions.

Page 335

9.5 Arrows 2, 4, and 6 would change.

9.6 15 kJ + 45 kJ = 60 kJ

9.7 50 kJ – 35 kJ = 15 kJ

9.8 –35 kJ The absolute value of ΔH is the same for the forward and reverse reactions.

9.9 The catalyst increases the rate of the reverse reaction because the catalyst lowers the energy of activation for the forward and reverse reactions.

Chapter Review

Page 335

1. (1)	2. (2)	3. (1)	4. (3)
5. (2)	6. (2)	7. (1)	8. (2)
9. (3)	10. (3)	11. (2)	12. (1)
13. (3)	14. (4)	15. (1)	16. (2)
17. (1)	18. (1)	19. (4)	20. (4)
21. (3)	22. (3)	23. (4)	24. (2)

25. (1) 40 kJ + 15 kJ = 55 kJ

26. (2) 25 kJ – 80 kJ = 55 kJ

Constructed Response

Page 339

1. (a) (b)

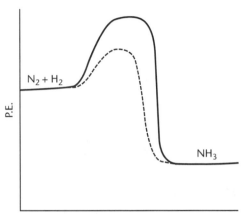

(c) Strong bonds take more energy to break, producing a high activation energy.
(d) +92 kJ

2. Increase the concentration of hydrogen peroxide. Raise the temperature. Add a catalyst.

CHAPTER 10

Practice

Page 347

Reaction:	A	+ 2B	→ C	+ 3D
Initial	1	1	0	0
Change	−0.4	−0.8	+.04	+1.2
Equilibrium	0.6	0.2	0.4	1.2

10.1 B is 0.2 mole, C is 0.4 mole, and D is 1.2 moles.

10.2 When the bottle is resealed, CO_2 continues to come out of solution until a new equilibrium is established and the fizzing stops.

Page 349

10.3 (a) Additional SO_3 would result in concentration of SO_2 increasing.
(b) Removal of O_2 would result in an increase in SO_2 concentration.

Page 351

10.4 (a) $\dfrac{[NH_3]^2}{[N_2][H_2]^3}$

(b) $\dfrac{[HF]^2[Cl_2]}{[F_2][HCl]^2}$

(c) $\dfrac{[CO][H_2]}{[H_2O]^2}$

Page 354

10.5 (a) An increase in pressure would decrease the amount of chlorine.
(b) An increase in pressure would decrease the amount of chlorine.
(c) An increase in pressure would not affect the amount of chlorine.
(d) An increase in the volume would increase the amount of chlorine.

10.6 The equilibrium would not be affected. The volume decreased, therefore the concentration of SO_2 and NO_2 would increase, although the amounts of both gases remain the same.

Page 358

10.7 (a) The concentration of O_2 would increase.
(b) The concentration of CO_2 would decrease.
(c) The value of the K_{EQ} would decrease.

10.8 (a) Decreasing temperature would increase concentration of O^2.
(b) Decreasing temperature would decrease concentration of NO.
(c) Decreasing temperature would decrease the value of the equilibrium constant.

Page 362

10.9 (a) oxygen increases
(b) oxygen decreases
(c) oxygen decreases
(d) oxygen increases

10.10 You could increase temperature, decrease pressure (or increase volume), remove SO_2, or add more SO_3.

10.11 (a) $K_{SP} = [Ba^{2+}]\,[SO_4^{2-}]$
(b) $K_{SP} = [Li^+]^2\,[CO_3^{2-}]$
(c) $K_{SP} = [Fe^{3+}]\,[OH^-]^3$

10.12 $CaSO_4$, $ZnCO_3$, $AgBr$, AgI

10.13 A ($BaCl_2$) and B (K_2SO_4) would decrease the solubility of $BaSO_4$ because they each have an ion in common with $BaSO_4$.

Page 367

10.14 (a) $AgCl$
(b) $Cu(OH)_2$ and $BaSO_4$
(c) none

10.15 Reaction (c) would not go to completion.

10.16 (a) $CaBr_2$ is soluble.
(b) $Fe(OH)_3$ is insoluble.
(c) $KClO_3$ is soluble.
(d) $PbSO_4$ is insoluble.

10.17 $NiSO_4$ or the sulfate of almost any metal not in Groups 1 or 2

Page 371

10.18 $K_{EQ} = 1.5$

10.19 0.5 M

Page 373

10.20 (a) $K_{SP} = 7.40 \times 10^{-14}$
(b) $K_{SP} = 1.91 \times 10^{-13}$

10.21 The K_{SP} of $AgCl$ is 1.8×10^{-10}, so its solubility is the square root of that, or 1.3×10^{-5} M. The K_{SP} of Ag_2CrO_4 is 1.1×10^{-12}. The solubility is the cube root of one fourth of the K_{SP}, or 6.5×10^{-5} M. The silver chromate is more soluble.

Chapter Review

Page 373

1. (1)	**2.** (4)	**3.** (3)	**4.** (4)
5. (3)	**6.** (3)	**7.** (4)	**8.** (2)
9. (2)	**10.** (1)	**11.** (2)	**12.** (1)
13. (3)	**14.** (4)	**15.** (3)	**16.** (3)
17. (2)	**18.** (2)	**19.** (1)	**20.** (4)
21. (3)	**22.** (1)	**23.** (3)	**24.** (3)
25. (2)	**26.** (1)	**27.** (3)	**28.** (4)
29. (1)	**30.** (4)	**31.** (4)	**32.** (2)
33. (1)	**34.** (3)	**35.** (3)	**36.** (3)
37. (1)	**38.** (2)	**39.** (3)	

Chemistry Challenge

Page 379

1. (a)
2. (b)
3. (c)
4. (e)
5. (a)
6. (d)
7. (d)
8. (e)

CHAPTER 11

Practice

11.1 $\dfrac{+53.0 \text{ kJ}}{2} = +26.5 \text{ kJ}$

11.2 $\dfrac{80 \text{ g NaOH}}{40 \text{ g/mole}} = 2$ moles NaOH

$-44.51 \text{ kJ/mole} \times 2 \text{ moles} = 90 \text{ kJ}$

11.3 $NaCl(s) \xrightarrow{H_2O} Na^+(aq) + Cl^-(aq)$

$\Delta H = +3.88 \text{ kJ}$

Dissolving of NaCl shows the smallest change in potential energy.

11.4 $\dfrac{180 \text{ g}}{\text{mole}} \div 10 = 18.0 \text{ g}$

11.5 (a) Positive: gas has greater entropy than solid.
(b) Negative: the product contains fewer moles.
(c) Positive: the solid reactant yields products that are solution and gas.
(d) Positive: solution has more entropy than a pure solid.

11.6 O_3 has a higher entropy because it is a more complex molecule than O_2.

11.7 $Br_2(l)$ has the lowest entropy because liquids have lower entropies than do gases. $Br(g)$ has a lower entropy than $Br_2(g)$ because Br_2 molecule is larger than Br.

11.8 $2O_3 (g) \to 3O_2 (g)$

$(3 \times 205.0 \text{ J/K}) - (2 \times 237.6 \text{ J/K})$
$= +139.8 \text{ J/K}$

Yes, the system produces 3 moles of product.

11.9 (a) The reaction is not spontaneous, because the potential energy is increasing while the entropy is decreasing. Both factors are unfavorable.
(b) Sign ΔG is +.

11.10 At room temperature:
ΔH is negative.
ΔS is negative.
ΔG is negative because the reaction is spontaneous at room temperature.

11.11 (a) $2\, NO(g) + O_2(g) \to 2\, NO_2(g)$

$\Delta H^0 = \Delta H^0_f$ products $- \Delta H^0_f$ reactants

$2(+33.84 \text{ kJ}) - [2(+90.37 \text{ kJ}) + 0 \text{ kJ}]$

$\Delta H^0 = -113.1 \text{ kJ}$

(b) $CH_4(g) + 2O_2(g) \to CO_2(g) + 2H_2O(l)$

$\Delta H^0 = \Delta H^0_f$ products $- \Delta H^0_f$ reactants

$[-393.5 + 2(-285.83)] - (-74.8) = -890.4 \text{ kJ}$

(c) $2\, CH_3OH(l) + 3\, O_2(g) \to 2\, CO_2(g) + 4\, H_2O(l)$

$\Delta H^0 = \Delta H^0_f$ products $- \Delta H^0_f$ reactants

$= [2(238.6 \text{ kJ}) + 0 \text{ kJ}] - [2(-393.5 \text{ kJ}) + 4(-285.83 \text{ kJ})]$

$= +1453 \text{ kJ}$

11.12 $2\, NO(g) + O_2(g) \to 2\, NO_2$

$\Delta G^\circ = \Delta G^\circ$ products $- \Delta G^\circ$ reactants

$2(+51.84 \text{ kJ}) - 2(+86.71 \text{ kJ})$
$= -69.74 \text{ kJ}$

11.13 $\Delta G^\circ = \Delta H^\circ - T\Delta S^\circ$

-69.74 kJ $= -113.1$ kJ $- 298$ K(ΔS)

$$\frac{-69.74 \text{ kJ} + 113.1 \text{ kJ}}{-298 \text{ K}} = \Delta S = -0.145 \text{ kJ/K}$$

11.14. NO(g) should be least stable.

Chapter Review

Page 399

1. (1)	**2.** (3)*	**3.** (4)	**4.** (3)
5. (1)	**6.** (1)	**7.** (1)	**8.** (2)
9. (1)	**10.** (2)	**11.** (1)	**12.** (1)
13. (1)	**14.** (3)	**15.** (4)	**16.** (2)
17. (4)	**18.** (2)	**19.** (3)	**20.** (4)
21. (2)	**22.** (2)	**23.** (2)	**24.** (2)
25. (3)	**26.** (2)		

*This one is tricky. According to the table, one mole of C_2H_5OH produces 1367 kJ. The value given for CH_3OH is 1452 kJ for two moles. So, it would be just 726 kJ for one mole. Similarly, the value given for the aluminum is for four moles. One mole of aluminum would produce 838 kJ.

Chemistry Challenge

Page 403

1. (a)
2. (d)
3. (a)
4. (e)
5. (c)
6. (e)
7. (c)
8. (c)
9. (b)
10. (a)

CHAPTER 12

Practice

Page 410

12.1 (a) hypochlorous acid
(b) hydrosulfuric acid
(c) oxalic acid
(d) phosphoric acid
(e) boric acid

Page 413

12.2 pH phosphoric acid = 2

12.3 (3) 100 times more basic

12.4 pH of KOH = 13

12.5 The pH of 0.1M NaCl solution is 7 because NaCl is a salt, not an acid or a base.

Page 414

12.6 (a) blue
(b) pink
(c) yellow
(d) red

12.7 The pH of pure water, 7.0, is in the middle of the range of bromthymol blue. The green color is a blend of the acidic yellow and the basic blue colors.

12.8 Alizarin yellow

12.9 Add magnesium to both solutions. Magnesium reacts with HCl but not NaOH.

Page 415

12.10 (a) pH = $-\log$ [H$^+$]
pH = $-\log$ 0.050
pH = 1.3

(b) [H$^+$] = 1.0×10^{-4}
pH = 4

12.11 $\text{pH} = -\log[\text{H}^+]$
$2.7 = -\log[\text{H}^+]$
$10^{-2.7} = [\text{H}^+]$
$1.99 \times 10^{-3} = 0.002\ M$

Page 416

12.12 (a) $\log 0.0020 = -2.7$
$-2.7 + 14 = 11.3$
$\text{pH} = 11.3$

(b) $\log 1.0 \times 10^{-5} = -5$
$-5 + 14 = 9$
$\text{pH} = 9$

(c) $\log 5 \times 10^{-12} = 12.7$
$-11.3 + 14 = 2.69 = 2.7$
$\text{pH} = 2.7$

12.13 $\text{pH} = 6$, $[\text{OH}] = 1 \times 10^{-8}$

Page 421

12.14 $M \times V\ (\text{H}^+) = M \times V\ (\text{OH}^-)$
$0.20\ M \times x = 0.1\ M \times 40\ \text{mL}$
$x = 20\ \text{mL KOH}$

12.15 $M \times V\ (\text{H}^+) = M \times V\ (\text{OH}^-)$
$0.40\ M \times 30\ \text{mL} = x \times 40\ \text{mL}$
$x = 0.30\ M\ \text{NaOH}$

12.16 $M \times V\ (\text{H}^+) = M \times V\ (\text{OH}^-)$
$0.5\ M \times 2\ \text{H}^+/\text{mole} \times 25\ \text{mL} =$
$0.40\ M \times 2\ \text{OH}^-/\text{mole} \times x$
$x = 31\ \text{mL Ba(OH)}_2$

Page 425

12.17 (a) $\text{HNO}_2 + \text{H}_2\text{O} \leftrightarrow \text{H}_3\text{O} + \text{NO}_2^-$

   acid 1   base 2   acid 2   base 1

(b) $\text{PO}^{3-} + \text{HF} \leftrightarrow \text{HPO}_4^{2-}\ \text{F}^-$

   base 2   acid 1   acid 2   base 1

12.18 (a) H_2O
(b) H_2PO_4^-
(c) HC_2O_4^-

12.19 (a) H_2O
(b) H_2PO_4^-
(c) SO_4^{2-}

Page 429

12.20 The amphiprotic ions are HSO_4^-, HS^-, HCO_3^-, H_2PO_4^-, and HPO_4^{2-}.

12.21 Cl^-

Page 430

12.22 $\dfrac{[\text{H}^+][\text{OH}^-]}{[\text{HNO}_3]} = K_a = 4.6 \times 10^{-4}$

$\dfrac{x^2}{0.5} = 4.6 \times 10^{-4}$

$x^2 = 2.3 \times 10^{-4}$

$x = 0.015$

$\text{pH} = 1.82$

$[\text{H}^+] = 0.015\ M$

12.23 $\text{HA} \leftrightarrow \text{H}^+ + \text{A}^-$, $\text{pH} = 3$
$[\text{H}^+] = [\text{A}^-] = 1.0 \times 10^{-3}$

$K_a = \dfrac{[\text{H}^+][\text{A}^-]}{[\text{HA}]}$

$\dfrac{1 \times 10^{-3} \times 1 \times 10^{-3}}{1} =$
$K_a = 1 \times 10^{-6}$

$\dfrac{x^2}{0.1} = 1 \times 10^{-7}$

$x = 1 \times 10^{-3.5}$

$\text{pH} = 3.5$

Page 432

12.24 (a) neutral
(b) basic
(c) basic
(d) acidic
(e) acidic
(f) acidic

12.25 $\text{PO}_4^{3-} + \text{H}_2\text{O} \rightarrow \text{HPO}_4^{2-} + \text{OH}^-$

Chapter Review

1. (3)	2. (2)	3. (2)	4. (1)
5. (3)	6. (4)	7. (4)	8. (2)
9. (3)	10. (1)	11. (2)	12. (4)
13. (2)	14. (4)	15. (3)	16. (3)
17. (3)	18. (4)	19. (2)	20. (3)
21. (1)	22. (2)	23. (1)	24. (4)
25. (2)	26. (4)	27. (3)	28. (1)
29. (3)	30. (3)	31. (1)	32. (4)
33. (3)	34. (3)	35. (4)	36. (3)
37. (3)	38. (2)		

Constructed Response

Page 437

1. The nitric acid will have a lower pH; you could test it with a pH meter or universal indicator paper. The nitric acid will be a better conductor of electricity; you could test it with a conductivity apparatus. In addition, acetic has a distinctive odor, the odor of vinegar.

2. $V \times M$ = moles

$$1 \text{ mL} \times \frac{L}{1000 \text{ mL}} \times \frac{0.0100 \text{ mole}}{L}$$

$$= 1 \times 10^{-5} \text{ mole } HNO_3$$

$$1 \times 10^{-5} \text{ mole } HNO_3 \times$$

$$\frac{1000 \text{ mL}}{1L} \times \frac{1}{100 \text{ mL}} = 1 \times 10^{-4}$$

pH = 4

3. Only the $Ba(OH)_2$ dissociates to produce hydroxide ions.

4. (a) 40 mL
   (b) 30 mL

CHAPTER 13

Practice

Page 447

13.1 (a) $2e^- + Sn^{4+} \rightarrow Sn^{2+}$
   (b) $Cl_2 + 2e^- \rightarrow 2 Cl^-$
   (c) $+6e^- + IO_3^- + 6 H^+ \rightarrow$
      $3 H_2O + I^-$

13.2 (a) $Zn \rightarrow Zn^{2+} + 2e^-$ Oxidation
      $2 H^+ + 2e^- \rightarrow H_2$ Reduction
   (b) $Mg \rightarrow Mg^{2+} + 2e^-$ Oxidation
      $S + 2e^- \rightarrow S^{2-}$ Reduction
   (c) $Cu \rightarrow Cu^{2+} + 2e^-$ Oxidation
      $S^{6+} + 2e^- \rightarrow S^{4+}$ Reduction

13.3 (a) $Pb^{2+} \rightarrow Pb^{4+} + 2e^-$ Oxidation
   (b) $As^{5+} + 2e^- \rightarrow As^{3+}$ Reduction
   (c) $P_4 \rightarrow 4P^{5+} + 20e^-$ Oxidation
   (d) $MnO_4^- + 8 H^+ + 5e^- \rightarrow$
      $Mn^{2+} + 4 H_2O$ Reduction

13.4 (a) Sn^{4+}
   (b) Cl_2
   (c) Zn^{2+}
   (d) I^{5+}, or IO_3^-

13.5 (a) Zn
   (b) I^-
   (c) S^{4+}, or SO_2
   (d) Fe^{2+}

Page 450

13.6 (a) Yes
   (b) No
   (c) Yes
   (d) Yes

13.7 Mn

Page 455

13.8 (a) $Pb^{2+} + 2e^- \rightarrow Pb$
   (b) $Cd \rightarrow Cd^{2+} + 2e^-$
   (c) Electrons flow from the Cd to the Pb.
   (d) Pb will increase in mass.

13.9

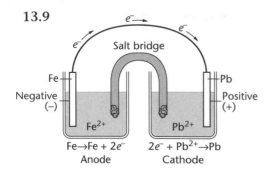

Fe | Negative (−) | Fe²⁺ | Fe→Fe + 2e⁻ | Anode
Pb | Positive (+) | Pb²⁺ | 2e⁻ + Pb²⁺→Pb | Cathode
Salt bridge

13.10 (a) 0 volts
(b) Mg would decrease.
(c) Mg^{2+} concentration would increase.

Page 459

13.11 (a) $2\ Cl^- \rightarrow Cl_2 + 2e^-$
(b) $K^+ + e^- \rightarrow K$
(c) $2\ K^+ + 2\ Cl^- \rightarrow 2\ K + Cl_2$

Page 466

13.12 (a) $2(Al \rightarrow Al^{3+} + 3e^-)$
$3(Fe^{2+} + 2e^- \rightarrow Fe)$
$2\ Al + 3\ Fe^{2+} \rightarrow 2\ Al^{3+} + 3\ Fe$

(b) $Cl_2 + 2e^- \rightarrow 2\ Cl^-$
$2\ Br^- \rightarrow Br_2 + 2e^-$
$Cl_2 + 2\ Br^- \rightarrow 2\ Cl^- + Br_2$

(c) $4(Al \rightarrow Al^{3+} + 3e^-)$
$3(Sn^{4+} + 4e^- \rightarrow Sn)$
$4\ Al + 3\ Sn^{4+} \rightarrow 4\ Al^{3+} + 3\ Sn$

(d) $Na \rightarrow Na^+ + e^-$
$2\ H^+ + 2e^- \rightarrow H_2$
$2\ Na + 2\ H^+ \rightarrow 2\ Na^+ + H_2$
$2\ Na + 2H_2O \rightarrow 2\ Na^+ + 2\ OH^- + H_2$

13.13 (a) $2(NO_3^- + 3e^- \rightarrow NO)$
$3(Cu \rightarrow Cu^{2+} + 2e^-)$

$8\ H^+ + 2\ NO_3^- + 3\ Cu \rightarrow 3\ Cu^{2+} + 2\ NO + 4\ H_2O$

(b) $4(Zn \rightarrow Zn^{2+} + 2e^-)$
$S^{6+} + 8e^- \rightarrow S^{2-}$

$4\ Zn + 5\ H_2SO_4 \rightarrow 4\ ZnSO_4 + H_2S + 4\ H_2O$

(c) $3(S^{4+} \rightarrow S^{6+} + 2e^-)$
$Cl^{5+} + 6e^- \rightarrow Cl$

$3\ SO + ClO^{3-} + 3\ H_2O \rightarrow 3\ SO_4^{2-} + Cl^- + 6\ H^+$

(d) $6(Fe^{2+} \rightarrow Fe^{3+} + e^-)$
$2\ Cr^{6+} + 6e^- \rightarrow 2\ Cr^{3+}$

$6\ Fe^{2+} + 14\ H^+ + Cr_2O_7^{2-} \rightarrow 2\ Cr^{3+} + 6\ Fe^{3+} + 7\ H_2O$

(e) $Sn^{2+} \rightarrow Sn^{4+} + 2e^-$
$2\ O^- + 2e^- \rightarrow 2\ O^{2-}$

$H_2O_2 + 2\ H^+ + Sn^{2+} \rightarrow Sn^{4+} + 2\ H_2O$

Page 471

13.14 (a) yes
(b) no
(c) yes

13.15 (a) yes
(b) yes
(c) yes
(d) no

Page 474

13.16

(a) $Cl_2 + 2e^- \rightarrow 2\ Cl^-$ $E^0 = +1.36$ volts
   $2\ Br^- \rightarrow Br_2 + 2e^-$ $E^0 = \underline{-1.06\ volts}$
   spontaneous   net $E^0 = +0.30$ volt

(b) $Cu \rightarrow Cu^{2+} + 2e^-$ $E^0 = -0.34$ volt
   $Ag^+ + e^- \rightarrow Ag$ $E^0 = \underline{+0.80\ volt}$
   spontaneous   net $E^0 = +0.46$ volt

(c) $Zn \rightarrow Zn^{2+} + 2e^-$ $E^0 = +0.76$ volts
   $Mg^{2+} + 2e^- \rightarrow Mg$ $E^0 = \underline{-2.37\ volts}$
not spontaneous   net $E^0 = -1.61$ volts

(d) $Cu \rightarrow Cu^{2+} + 2e^-$ $E^0 = -0.34$ volts
   $2e^- + Cl_2 \rightarrow 2\ Cl^-$ $E^0 = \underline{+1.36\ volts}$
   spontaneous   net $E^0 = +1.02$ volts

(e) $Cr_2O_7^{2-} + 14\ H^+ + 6e^- \rightarrow$
   $2\ Cr^{3+} + 7\ H_2O$ $E^0 = +1.33$ volts
   $Sn^{2+} \rightarrow Sn^{4+} + 2e^-$ $E^0 = \underline{-0.15\ volts}$
   spontaneous   net $E^0 = +1.18$ volts

Page 476

13.17 (a) $2(NO_3^- + 3\ e^- + 4\ H^+ \rightarrow NO + 2\ H_2O)$
$3(Cu \rightarrow Cu^{2+} + 2e^-)$
$2\ NO_3^- + 8\ H^+ + 3\ Cu \rightarrow 2\ NO + 3\ Cu^{2+} + 4\ H_2O$

(b) $3(SO_2 + 2 H_2O \rightarrow SO_4^{2-} + 4 H^+ + 2e^-)$

$6e^- + ClO_3^- + 6 H^+ \rightarrow Cl^- + 3 H_2O$

$3 SO_2 + 3 H_2O + ClO_3^- \rightarrow 3 SO_4^{2-} + 6 H^+ + Cl^-$

(c) $6(Fe^{2+} \rightarrow Fe^{3+} + e^-)$

$6e^- + Cr_2O_7^{2-} + 14 H+ \rightarrow 2 Cr^{3+} + 7 H_2O$

$6 Fe^{2+} + Cr_2O_7^{2-} + 14 H^+ \rightarrow 6 Fe^{3+} + 2 Cr^{3+} + 7 H_2O$

Chapter Review

Page 478

1. (4)	2. (1)	3. (4)	4. (4)
5. (3)	6. (3)	7. (2)	8. (1)
9. (3)	10. (1)	11. (4)	12. (2)
13. (2)	14. (1)	15. (2)	16. (2)
17. (2)	18. (1)	19. (3)	20. (4)
21. (1)	22. (3)	23. (3)	24. (2)
25. (1)	26. (3)	27. (1)	28. (1)
29. (4)	30. (1)	31. (4)	32. (2)
33. (1)	34. (3)	35. (3)	36. (1)
37. (1)	38. (2)	39. (4)	40. (2)
41. (3)	42. (4)	43. (3)	44. (3)
45. (2)	46. (4)	47. (4)	48. (2)
49. (4)	50. (3)	51. (4)	52. (3)

Constructed Response

Page 485

1.

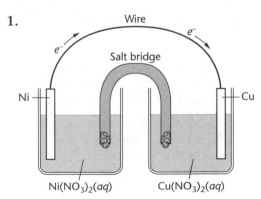

Wire, salt bridge

2. (a) Electrons flow from nickel to copper.
   (b) Cu^{2+} is reduced.
   (c) $Ni \rightarrow Ni^{2+} + 2e^-$

3. The blue color of Cu^{2+} will fade while the green color of Ni^{2+} will deepen.

4. (a) The oxidation state of Fe is zero.
   (b) The oxygen is −2.
   (c) $4 Fe \rightarrow 4 Fe^{3+} + 12e^-$

5. (a) $Zn^{2+} + 2e^- \rightarrow Zn$
   (b) $Al \rightarrow Al^{3+} + 3e^-$
   (c) $3 Zn^{2+} + 2 Al \rightarrow 3 Zn + 2 Al^{3+}$
   (d) The reduction of the zinc ion occurs at the cathode.

CHAPTER 14

Practice

Page 494

14.1 (a) C_4H_8
     (b) C_8H_{18}
     (c) C_6H_{10}
     (d) $C_{10}H_{22}$

14.2 (a) alkane
     (b) alkyne
     (c) alkene

Page 501

14.3

(a)
```
    H  H  H  H  H
    |  |  |  |  |
H — C — C = C — C — C — H
    |        |  |
    H        H  H
```

(b)
```
             H
             |
         H — C — H
    H        H  H
    |        |  |
H — C = C — C — C — C — H
    |   |   |  |  |
    H   H   H  H  H
```

(c) 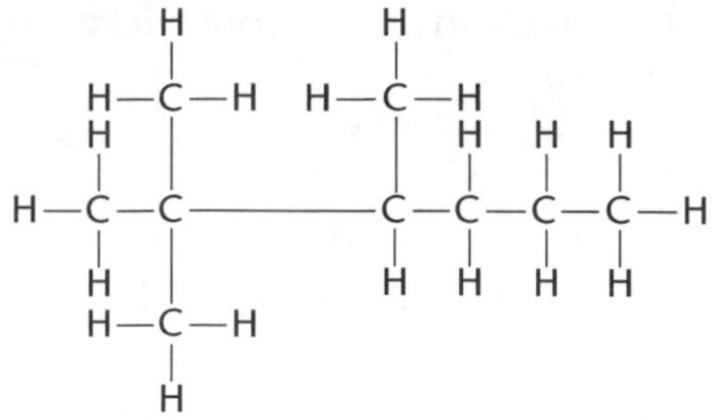 [chemical structure diagram]

(d) 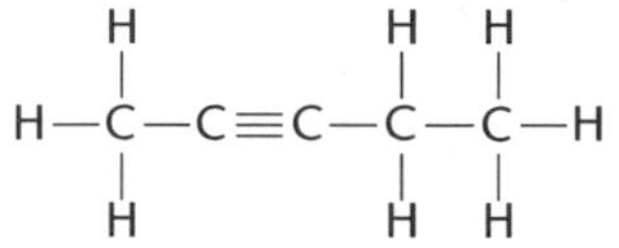 [chemical structure diagram]

(d) [chemical structure diagram]

(e) [chemical structure diagram]

(f) [chemical structure diagram]

(g) [chemical structure diagram]

14.4 (a) 1-pentene
 (b) 1-butyne
 (c) 3,3-dimethylhexane
 (d) ethyne

14.5 (a) 2-methylepentane (Other answers are possible.)
 (b) pentane, also 2-methylbutane
 (c) 2-butene

Page 506

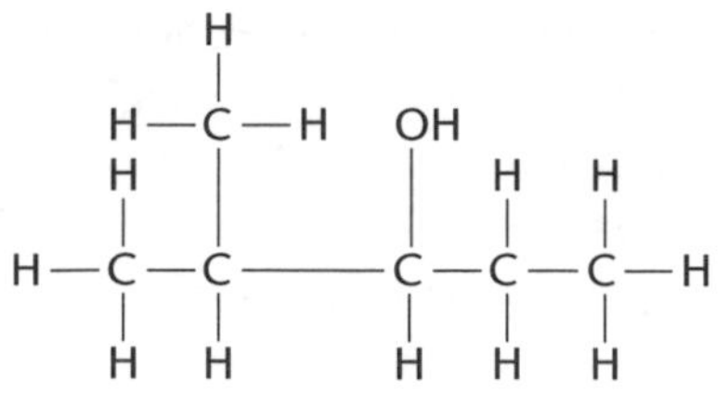

14.6 (a) propanal
 (b) 2-methylbutane
 (c) 1,1,1-trichloroethane
 (d) 1-butyne
 (e) 3-pentanone

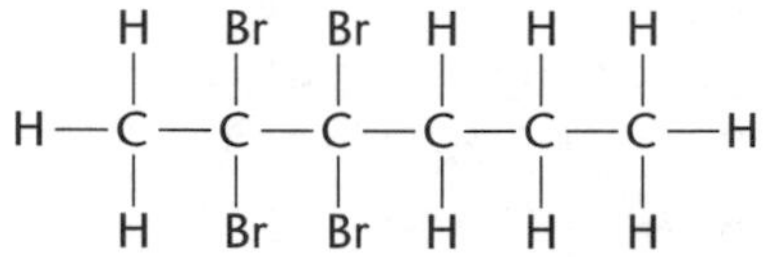

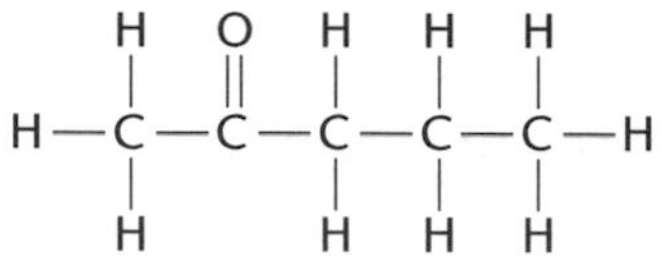

14.7

(a) 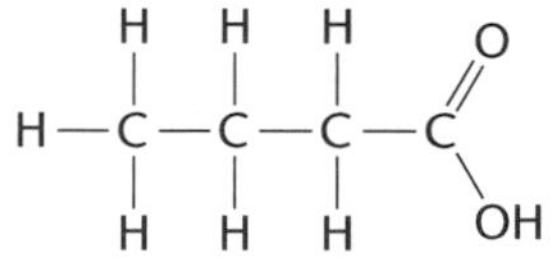 [chemical structure diagram]

(b) 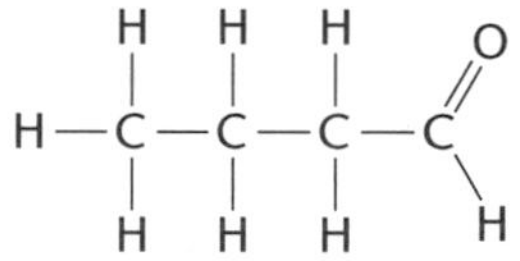 [chemical structure diagram]

(c) 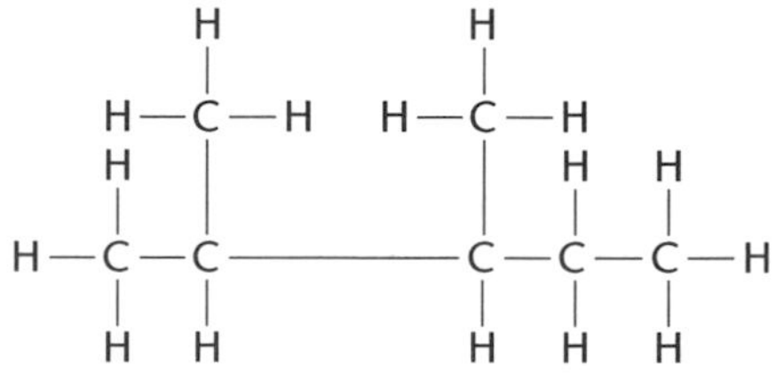 [chemical structure diagram]

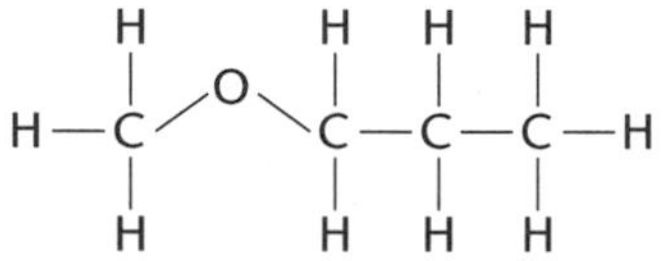

14.8 If the oxygen is on the end carbon, the resulting structure is propanal.

Page 512

14.9 (a) CH_3Cl +HCl, chloromethane + hydrogen chloride
 (b) $C_4H_8Br_2$, 2,3-dibromobutane
 (c) C_2H_5Cl + HCl, chloroethane + hydrogen chloride
 (d) C_3H_8, propane
 (e) $C_2H_2Br_4$, 1,1,2,2-tetrabromo-ethane

Page 519

14.10 (a) $C_3H_6Cl_2$, 1,2-dichloro-propane
 (b) $2 H_2O$, water
 (c) $2 CO_2$, carbon dioxide
 (d) C_2H_5Cl, chloroethane
 (e) $C_3H_5(OH)_3$, glycerol

14.11 (a) CH_3OH, methanol
 (b) C_2H_2, ethyne
 (c) C_4H_{10}, butane
 (d) C_3H_8, propane

14.12

(a)

```
        O    H   H
        ‖    |   |
   H —— C —— O —— C —— C —— H
             |   |
             H   H
```

(b)

```
    H   H   H   O        H   H
    |   |   |   ‖        |   |
H — C — C — C — C — O — C — C — H
    |   |   |             |   |
    H   H   H             H   H
```

(c)

```
   OH  OH  OH
    |   |   |
H — C — C — C — H
    |   |   |
    H   H   H
```

(d)

```
    H   Br  Br  H
    |   |   |   |
H — C — C — C — C — H
    |   |   |   |
    H   H   H   H
```

Page 524

14.13 (a) alkene
     (b) secondary alcohol
     (c) ketone
     (d) aldehyde
     (e) alkane

14.14

(a)

```
    H   H   H   H
    |   |   |   |
H — C — C — C — C — H
    |   |   |   |
    H   H   H   H
```

(b)

```
                H
                |
H — C ≡ C — C — H
                |
                H
```

(c)

```
   OH  H   H   H
    |   |   |   |
H — C — C — C — C — H
    |   |   |   |
    H   H   H   H
```

(d)

```
 H      H   H   H   H
  \     |   |   |   |
   C = C — C — C — C — H
  /         |   |   |
 H          H   H   H
```

Page 529

14.15

```
    H   H   H   H   H   H
    |   |   |   |   |   |
H — C — C — C — C — C — C — H
    |   |   |   |   |   |
    H   H   H   H   H   H
```
hexane

```
            H
            |
       H — C — H
            |
    H   H       H   H   H
    |   |       |   |   |
H — C — C ————— C — C — C — H
    |   |       |   |   |
    H   H       H   H   H
```
2-methylpentane

```
                H
                |
           H — C — H
    H   H       H   H
    |   |       |   |
H — C — C ————— C — C — C — H
    |   |       |   |   |
    H   H       H   H   H
```
3-methylpentane

```
       H             H
       |             |
  H — C — H     H — C — H
       H             H
       |             |
H — C — C ————— C — C — H
    |   |       |   |
    H   H       H   H
```
2,3-dimethylbutane

```
            H
            |
       H — C — H
    H       |       H   H
    |       |       |   |
H — C ————— C ————— C — C — H
    |       |       |   |
    H       |       H   H
       H — C — H
            |
            H
```
2,2-dimethylbutane

14.16

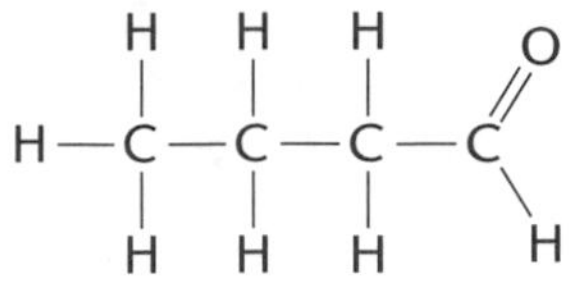

H—C—C—C—C butanal
(with H's and O)

(There are other possibilities.)

Chapter Review

Page 530

Constructed Response

Page 535

1.

(a)

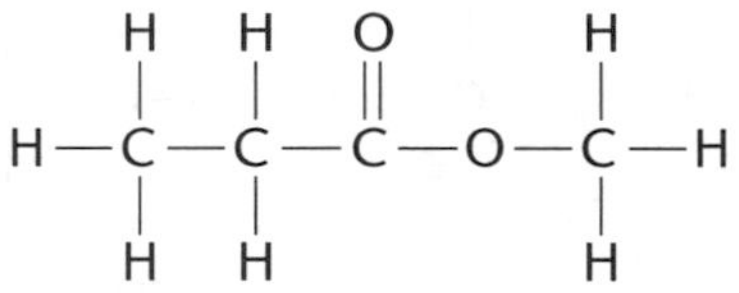

(b)

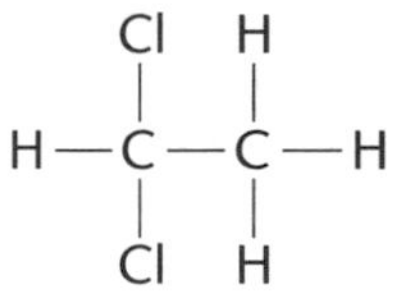

(c)

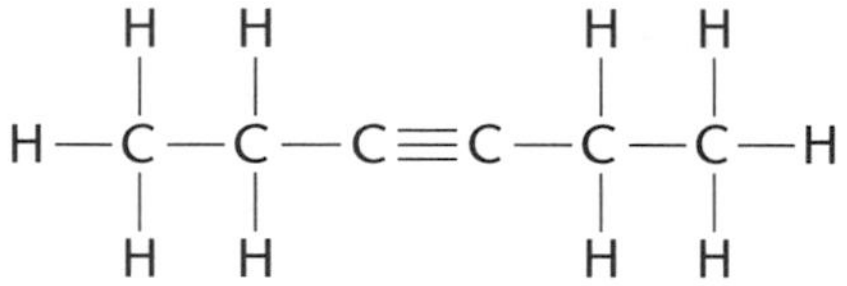

(d)

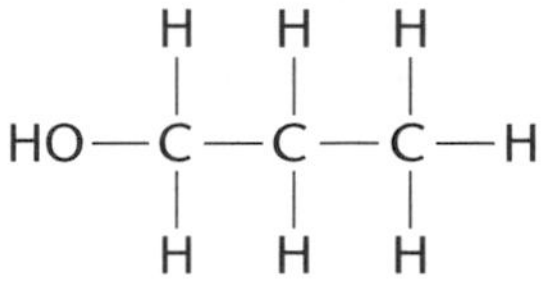

(e)

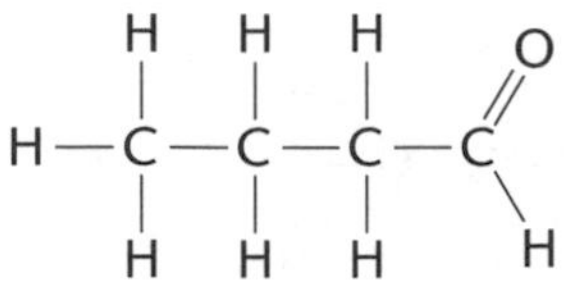

(f)

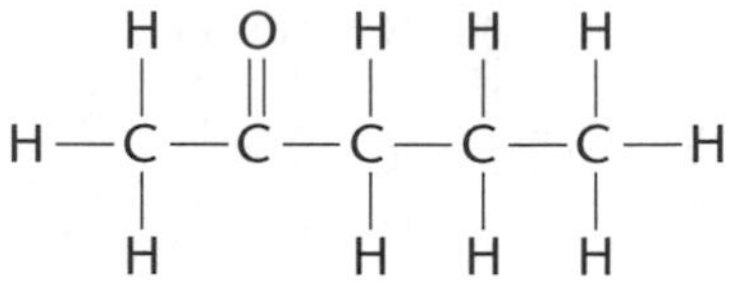

2. Compound

(1) 2-butanol

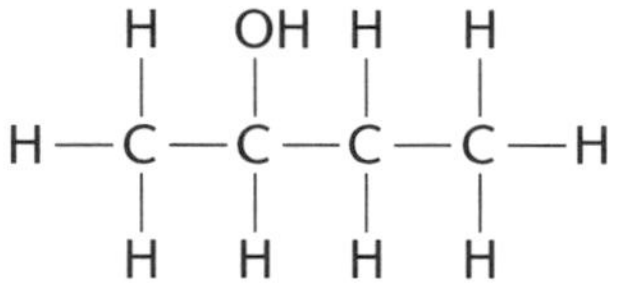

(a)

Isomer

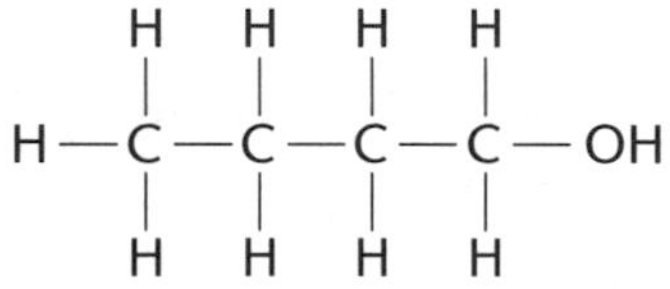

(b)

(c) 1-butanal
(Other answers are possible, including 2-methyl-2 propanol.)

Compound

(2) propanal

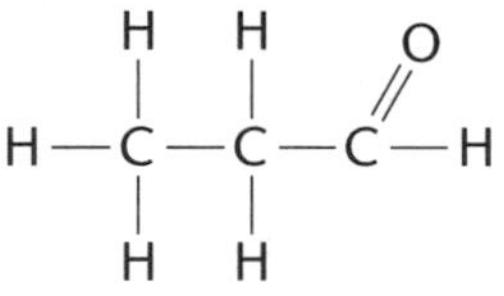

(a)

Isomer

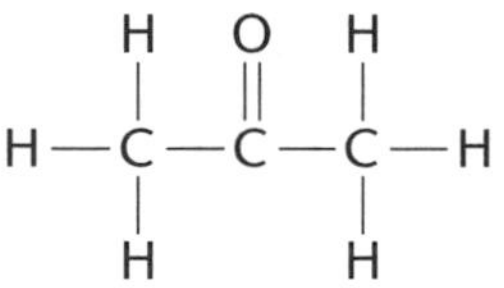

(b)

(c) 2-propanone

Compound

(3) ethoxyethane, or diethyl ether

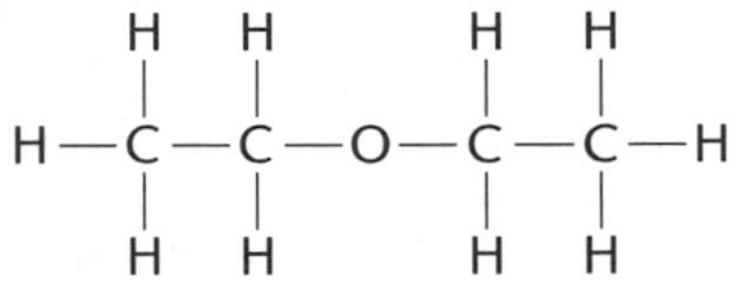

(a)

Isomer

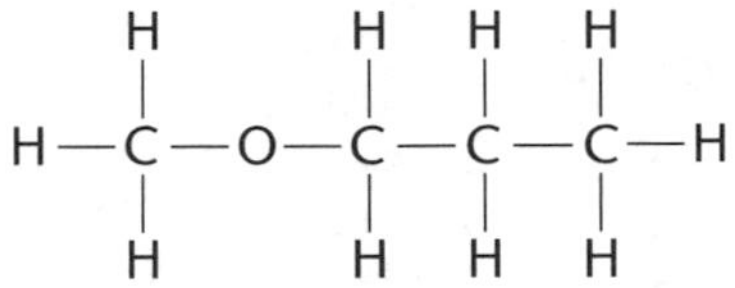

(b)

(c) methoxy propane
(Other answers are possible, including 1- or 2-butanol.)

Compound

(4) methyl ethanoate, or methyl acetate

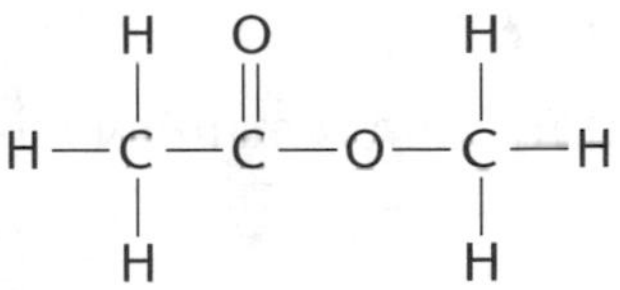

(a)

Isomer

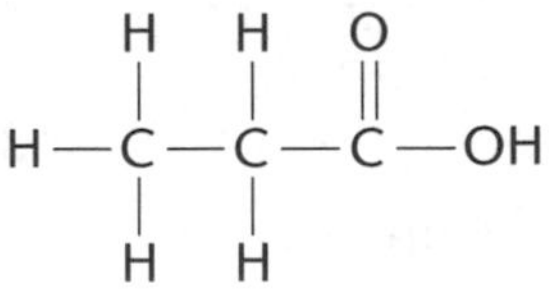

(b)

(c) propanoic acid

CHAPTER 15

Practice

Page 546

15.1 (a) $^{60}_{27}CO \rightarrow {}^{0}_{-1}e + {}^{60}_{28}Ni$

(b) $^{238}_{92}U \rightarrow {}^{4}_{2}He + {}^{234}_{90}Th$

(c) $^{42}_{19}K \rightarrow {}^{0}_{-1}e + {}^{42}_{20}Ca$

(d) $^{37}_{19}K \rightarrow {}^{0}_{+1}e + {}^{37}_{18}Ar$

15.2 (a) $^{4}_{2}He$

(b) $^{0}_{-1}e$

(c) $^{228}_{88}Ra$

(d) $^{99}_{44}Ru$

Page 548

15.3 (a) $^{239}_{93}Np$

(b) $^{17}_{8}O$

(c) $^{239}_{94}Pu$

(d) $^{190}_{36}Kr$

15.4 (c)

Page 552

15.5 fraction remaining $= \left(\dfrac{1}{2}\right)^{\frac{t}{T}}$

$$\frac{1}{16} = \left(\frac{1}{2}\right)^4$$

$$\frac{t}{T} = 4$$

$$\frac{t}{1600} = 4$$

$$t = 6400 \text{ years}$$

15.6 CO – 60, T = 5.26 years

$$\text{fraction remaining} = \left(\frac{1}{2}\right)^{\frac{t}{T}}$$

$$= \left(\frac{1}{2}\right)^{\frac{15.78}{5.26}}$$

$$= \left(\frac{1}{2}\right)^{3}$$

$$= \frac{1}{8}$$

$$\frac{1}{8} \times 200 \text{ g} = 25 \text{ g}$$

15.7 $\text{fraction remaining} = \left(\frac{1}{2}\right)^{\frac{t}{T}}$

$$\frac{4.0}{64} = \left(\frac{1}{2}\right)^{\frac{t}{T}}$$

$$\frac{1}{16} = \left(\frac{1}{2}\right)^{4}$$

$$\frac{t}{T} = 4$$

$$\frac{2 \text{ min}}{T} = 4$$

$$T = \frac{1}{2}\text{min}$$

Page 557

15.8 $W = {}^{1}_{0}n$

$x = {}^{238}_{92}U$

$Y = {}^{239}_{93}Np$

Page 563

15.9 (a) $\text{fraction remaining} = \left(\frac{1}{2}\right)^{\frac{t}{T}}$

$$= \left(\frac{1}{2}\right)^{\frac{3.10}{12.4}}$$

$$= \left(\frac{1}{2}\right)^{0.250}$$

$$= 0.841$$

$$0.841 \times 10.0 \text{ g} = 8.41 \text{ g}$$

(b) $\text{fraction remaining} = \left(\frac{1}{2}\right)^{\frac{t}{T}}$

$$= \left(\frac{1}{2}\right)^{\frac{18.6}{12.4}}$$

$$= \left(\frac{1}{2}\right)^{1.50} = 0.354$$

$$0.354 \times 10.0 \text{ g} = 3.54$$

Chapter Review

Page 563

1. (4)	2. (4)	3. (1)	4. (4)
5. (2)	6. (2)	7. (3)	8. (1)
9. (3)	10. (3)	11. (1)	12. (3)
13. (2)	14. (4)	15. (1)	16. (3)
17. (2)	18. (4)	19. (3)	20. (3)
21. (2)	22. (1)	23. (4)	24. (3)
25. (2)	26. (1)	27. (1)	28. (1)

Constructed Response

Page 567

1. (a) $\text{fraction remaining} = \left(\frac{1}{2}\right)^{\frac{t}{T}}$

$$\frac{1}{16} = \left(\frac{1}{2}\right)^{4}$$

$$\frac{t}{T} = 4$$

$$\frac{15.28 \text{ days}}{T} = 4$$

$$T = 3.82 \text{ days}$$

(b) ${}^{222}Rn$

2. (a) ${}^{238}_{92}U \rightarrow {}^{4}_{2}He + {}^{234}_{90}Th$

(b) ${}^{234}_{90}Th \rightarrow {}^{4}_{2}He + {}^{230}_{88}Ra$

$${}^{230}_{88}Ra \rightarrow {}^{4}_{2}He + {}^{226}_{86}Rn$$

$${}^{226}_{86}Rn \rightarrow {}^{0}_{-1}e + {}^{226}_{87}Fr$$

$${}^{226}_{87}Fr \rightarrow {}^{0}_{-1}e + {}^{226}_{88}Ra$$

3. (a) It is difficult to store nuclear wastes safely; accidents could contaminate the environment; nuclear power plants are possible targets for terrorists, etc.

(b) Longer lasting supply of fuel, no air pollution, no greenhouse gases produced, etc.

APPENDIX 1

Page 574

A.1 $125 \text{ mg} \times \dfrac{1 \text{ g}}{1000 \text{ mg}} = 0.125$

A.2 $250 \text{ mL} \times \dfrac{1 \text{ L}}{1000 \text{ mL}} = 0.25 \text{ L}$

A.3 $183 \text{ cm} \times \dfrac{1 \text{ m}}{100 \text{ cm}} = 1.83 \text{ m}$

A.4 $25.3 \text{ cm} \times \dfrac{1 \text{ m}}{100 \text{ cm}} \times \dfrac{1000 \text{ mm}}{1 \text{ m}} =$ 253 mm

A.5 $62{,}000. \text{ g} \times \dfrac{1 \text{ kg}}{1000 \text{ g}} \times \dfrac{2.2 \text{ lb}}{1 \text{ kg}} =$ 136 lb

Page 576

A.6

$$\% \text{ error} = \frac{\text{measured value} - \text{accepted value}}{\text{accepted value}} \times 100$$

$$\frac{18.0 \text{ amu} - 16.0 \text{ amu}}{16.0 \text{ amu}} \times 100 = 12.5\%$$

A.7

$$\% \text{ error} = \frac{\text{measured value} - \text{accepted value}}{\text{accepted value}} \times 100$$

$$\frac{189 \text{ lb} - 180. \text{ lb}}{180. \text{ lb}} \times 100 = 5.00\%$$

A.8

$$\% \text{ error} = \frac{\text{measured value} - \text{accepted value}}{\text{accepted value}} \times 100$$

$$+10.\% = \frac{x - 36\%}{36\%} \times 100$$

$$x = 39.6\%$$

$$-10\% = \frac{y - 36\%}{36\%}$$

$$y = 32.4\%$$

Page 578

A.9 (a) 3
(b) 3
(c) 2
(d) 4

A.10 (a) $5.51 \text{ g} \div 4.2 \text{ L} = 1.3 \text{ g/L}$
(b) $49.2 \text{ mL} - 48 \text{ mL} = 1 \text{ mL}$
(c) $101.3 \text{ kPa} \times 15.0 \text{ L} = 1520 \text{ kPa} \bullet \text{L}$

A.11 43 cm^3

A.12 Volume of water + metal
$$= 45.4 \text{ mL}$$
Volume of water $= -41.4 \text{ mL}$
Volume of metal $= 4.0 \text{ mL}$

$$\text{density} = \frac{\text{mass}}{\text{volume}}$$

$$= \frac{24.3 \text{ g}}{4.0 \text{ mL}} = 6.1 \text{ g/mL}$$

A.13 5.50 g

Correlation of *Contemporary Chemistry: The Physical Setting* to New York State's Physical Setting/Chemistry Core Curriculum

STANDARD 4: The Physical Setting

Students will understand and apply scientific concepts, principles, and theories pertaining to the physical setting and living environment and recognize the historical development of ideas in science.

Key Idea 3:

Matter is made up of particles whose properties determine the observable characteristics of matter and its reactivity.

Performance Indicator 3.1   Explain the properties of materials in terms of the arrangement and properties of the atoms that compose them.

Major Understanding	Textbook pp.
3.1a The modern model of the atom has evolved over a long period of time through the work of many scientists.	66–72, 80–83
3.1b Each atom has a nucleus, with an overall positive charge, surrounded by negatively charged electrons.	68–70
3.1c Subatomic particles contained in the nucleus include protons and neutrons.	70
3.1d The proton is positively charged, and the neutron has no charge. The electron is negatively charged.	70
3.1e Protons and electrons have equal but opposite charges. The number of protons equals the number of electrons in an atom.	10, 70, 99
3.1f The mass of each proton and each neutron is approximately equal to one atomic mass unit. An electron is much less massive than a proton or a neutron.	70
3.1g The number of protons in an atom (atomic number) identifies the element. The sum of the protons and neutrons in an atom (mass number) identifies an isotope.	70–71, 74
3.1h In the wave–mechanical model (electron cloud model) the electrons are in orbitals, which are defined as the regions of the most probable electron location (ground state).	76
3.1i Each electron in an atom has its own distinct amount of energy,	79
3.1j When an electron in an atom gains a specific amount of energy, the electron is at a higher energy state (excited state).	76, 80

Major Understanding	Textbook pp.
3.1k When an electron returns from a higher energy state to a lower energy state, a specific amount of energy is emitted. This emitted energy can be used to identify an element.	76–77, 80–82
3.1l The outermost electrons in an atom are called the valence electrons. In general, the number of valence electrons affects the chemical properties of an element.	97–98
3.1m Atoms of an element that contain the same number of protons but a different number of neutrons are called isotopes of that element.	73–74 539–540
3.1n The average atomic mass of an element is the weighted average of the masses of its naturally occurring isotopes.	71–76
3.1o Stability of an isotope is based on the ratio of neutrons and protons in its nucleus. Although most nuclei are stable, some are unstable and spontaneously decay, emitting radiation.	540–541, 560–561
3.1p Spontaneous decay can involve the release of alpha particles, beta particles, positrons, and/or gamma radiation from the nucleus of an unstable isotope.	539–540, 543–545
3.1q Matter is classified as a pure substance or as a mixture of substances.	10–11
3.1r A pure substance (element or compound) has a constant composition and constant properties throughout a given sample, and from sample to sample.	11
3.1s Mixtures are composed of two or more different substances that can be separated by physical means. When different substances are mixed together, a homogenous or heterogeneous mixture is formed.	12
3.1t The proportions of components in a mixture can be varied. Each component in a mixture retains its original properties.	12–13
3.1u Elements are substances that are composed of atoms that have the same atomic number. Elements cannot be broken down by chemical change.	10
3.1v Elements can be classified by their properties and located on the Periodic Table as metals, nonmetals, metalloids (B, Si, Ge, As, Sb, Te) and noble gases.	192–193
3.1w Elements can be differentiated by physical properties. Physical properties of substances, such as density, conductivity, malleability, solubility, and hardness, differ among elements.	5–6

Major Understanding	Textbook pp.
3.1x Elements can also be differentiated by chemical properties. Chemical properties describe how an element behaves during a chemical reaction.	5–6
3.1y The placement or location of an element on the Periodic Table gives an indication of the physical and chemical properties of that element. The elements on the Periodic Table are arranged in order of increasing atomic number.	186–187
3.1z For Groups 1, 2, and 13-18 on the Periodic Table, elements within the same group have the same number of valence electrons (helium is an exception) and therefore similar chemical properties.	190
3.1aa The succession of elements within the same group demonstrates characteristic trends: differences in atomic radius, ionic radius, electronegativity, first ionization energy, metallic/nonmetallic properties.	188–190
3.1bb The succession of elements across the same period demonstrates characteristic trends: differences in atomic radius, ionic radius, electronegativity, first ionization energy, metallic/nonmetallic properties.	187–190
3.1cc A compound is a substance composed of two or more different elements that are chemically combined in a fixed proportion. A chemical compound can be broken down by chemical means. A chemical compound can be represented by a specific chemical formula and assigned a name based on the IUPAC system.	10–11, 150–160, 163–164, 496–506
3.1dd Compounds can be differentiated by their physical and chemical properties.	11
3.1ee Types of chemical formulas include empirical, molecular, and structural.	156–159, 162–167, 490–491
3.1ff Organic compounds contain carbon atoms, which bond to one another in chains, rings, and networks to form a variety of structures.	488–489, 535–537
3.1gg Hydrocarbons are compounds that contain only carbon and hydrogen. Saturated hydrocarbons contain only single carbon–carbon bonds. Unsaturated hydrocarbons contain at least one multiple carbon–carbon bond.	138, 491–494, 510

Major Understanding	Textbook pp.
3.1hh Organic acids, alcohols, esters, aldehydes, ketones, ethers, halides, amines, amides, and amino acids are categories of organic compounds that differ in their structures. Functional groups impart distinctive physical and chemical properties to organic compounds.	494–496, 520–529
3.1ii Isomers of organic compounds have the same molecular formula, but different structures and properties.	507–510
3.1jj The structure and arrangement of particles and their interactions determine the physical state of a substance at a given temperature and pressure.	52–56
3.1kk The three phases of matter (solids, liquids, and gases) have different properties.	4–5, 23–24, 44–46, 50–52
3.1ll Entropy is a measure of the randomness or disorder of a system. A system with greater disorder has greater entropy.	390
3.1mm Systems in nature tend to undergo changes toward lower energy and higher entropy.	390, 392–393
3.1nn Differences in properties such as density, particle size, molecular polarity, boiling and freezing points, and solubility permit physical separation of the components of the mixture.	12
3.1oo A solution is a homogeneous mixture of a solute dissolved in a solvent. The solubility of a solute in a given amount of solvent is dependent on the temperature, the pressure, and the chemical natures of the solute and solvent.	284–285, 289–296
3.1pp The concentration of a solution may be expressed in molarity (M), percent by volume, percent by mass, or parts per million (ppm).	297–305
3.1qq The addition of a nonvolatile solute to a solvent causes the boiling point of the solution to increase and the freezing point of the solvent to decrease. The greater the concentration of solute particles, the greater the effect.	308–312, 315–316
3.1rr An electrolyte is a substance which, when dissolved in water, forms a solution capable of conducting an electric current. The ability of a solution to the conduct an electric current depends on the concentration of ions.	306–308, 312–313

Major Understanding	Textbook pp.
3.1ss The acidity or alkalinity of an aqueous solution can be measured by its pH value. The relative level of acidity or alkalinity of these solutions can be shown by using indicators.	412–414
3.1tt On the pH scale, each decrease of one unit of pH represents a tenfold increase in hydronium ion concentration.	412
3.1uu Behavior of many acids and bases can be explained by the Arrhenius theory. Arrhenius acids and bases are electrolytes.	407
3.1vv Arrhenius acids yield H^+ (aq), hydrogen ion as the only positive ion in an aqueous solution. The hydrogen ion may also be written as H_3O^+(aq), hydronium ion.	407–412
3.1ww Arrhenius bases yield OH–(aq), hydroxide ion as the only negative ion in an aqueous solution.	407–412
3.1xx In the process of neutralization, an Arrhenius acid and an Arrhenius base react to form a salt and water.	407, 416–417
3.1yy There are alternate acid–base theories. One theory states that an acid is an H^+ donor and a base is an H^+ acceptor.	417–421
3.1zz Titration is a laboratory process in which a volume of a solution of known concentration is used to determine the concentration of another solution.	417–421

Performance Indicator 3.2   Use atomic and molecular models to explain common chemical reactions.

Major Understanding	Textbook pp.
3.2a A physical change results in the rearrangement of existing particles in a substance. A chemical change results in the formation of different substances with changed properties.	6, 13
3.2b Types of chemical reactions include synthesis, decomposition, single replacement, and double replacement.	172–175
3.2c Types of organic reactions include addition, substitution, polymerization, esterification, fermentation, saponification, and combustion.	510–519
3.2d An oxidation-reduction (redox) reaction involves the transfer of electrons (e^-).	440–441, 444–447

Major Understanding	Textbook pp.
3.2e Reduction is the gain of electrons.	441, 444
3.2f A half–reaction can be written to represent reduction.	442
3.2g Oxidation us the loss of electrons.	441, 443–444
3.2h A half–reaction can be written to represent oxidation.	442
3.2i Oxidation numbers (states) can be assigned to atoms and ions. Changes in oxidation numbers indicate that oxidation and reduction have occurred.	442–444
3.2j An electrochemical cell can be either voltaic or electrolytic. In an electrochemical cell, oxidation numbers indicate that oxidation occurs at the anode and reduction at the cathode.	451–455
3.2k A voltaic cell spontaneously converts chemical energy to electrical energy.	455–457
3.2l An electrolytic cell requires electrical energy to produce a chemical change. This process is known as electrolysis.	457–459

Performance Indicator 3.3   Apply the principle of conservation of mass to chemical reactions.

Major Understanding	Textbook pp.
3.3a In all chemical reactions there is a conservation of mass, energy, and charge.	9, 16, 383–384
3.3b In a redox reaction the number of electrons lost is equal to the number of electrons gained.	440–442
3.3c A balanced chemical equation represents conservation of atoms. The coefficients in a balanced chemical equation can be used to determine mole ratios in the reaction.	169–172
3.3d The empirical formula of a compound is the simplest whole-number ratio of atoms of the elements in a compound. It may be different from the molecular formula, which is the actual ratio of atoms in a molecule of that compound.	162–163, 243–249
3.3e The formula mass of a substance is the sum of the atomic masses of its atoms. The molar mass (gram-formula mass) of a substance equals one mole of that substance.	167–168, 237–238

Major Understanding	Textbook pp.
3.3f The percent composition by mass of each element in a compound can be calculated mathematically.	240–243

Performance Indicator 3.4   Use kinetic molecular theory (KMT) to explain rates of reactions and the relationship among temperature, pressure, and volume of a substance.

Major Understanding	Textbook pp.
3.4a The concept of an ideal gas is a model to explain the behavior of gases. A real gas is most like an ideal gas when the real gas is at low pressure and high temperature.	38, 43–44
3.4b Kinetic molecular theory (KMT) for an ideal gas states that all particles are in random, constant, straight-line motion; are separated by great distances relative to their size; have no attractive forces between them; have collisions that may result in a transfer of energy between gas particles, but the total energy of the system remains constant.	24–27
3.4c Kinetic molecular theory describes the relationships of pressure, volume, temperature, velocity, frequency, and force of collisions among gas molecules.	27–39
3.4d Collision theory states that a reaction is most likely to occur if reactant particles collide with the proper energy and orientation.	323–326
3.4e Equal volumes of gases at the same temperature and pressure contain an equal number of particles.	39–40
3.4f The rate of a chemical reaction depends on several factors: temperature, concentration, nature of reactants, surface area, and the presence of a catalyst.	322–333
3.4g A catalyst provides an alternate reaction pathway, which has a lower activation energy than an uncatalyzed reaction.	330–332
3.4h Some chemical and physical changes can reach equilibrium.	342–343
3.4i At equilibrium the rate of the forward reaction equals the rate of the reverse reaction. The measurable quantities of reactants and products remain constant at equilibrium.	342–347
3.4j LeChatelier's principle can be used to predict the effect of stress (change of pressure, volume, concentration, and temperature) on a system at equilibrium.	348–361

Key Idea 4:

Energy exists in many forms, and when these forms change energy is conserved.

Performance Indicator 4.1   Observe and describe transmission of various forms of energy.

Major Understanding	Textbook pp.
4.1a Energy can exist in different forms, such as chemical, electrical, electromagnetic, thermal, mechanical, and nuclear.	13–14, 76, 539
4.1b Chemical and physical changes can be exothermic or endothermic.	20, 383–386
4.1c Energy released or absorbed during a chemical reaction can be represented by a potential energy diagram.	333–384, 117–118
4.1d Energy released or absorbed during a chemical reaction (heat of reaction) is equal to the difference between the potential energy of the products and the potential energy of the reactants.	324–325

Performance Indicator 4.2   Explain heat in terms of kinetic molecular theory.

Major Understanding	Textbook pp.
4.2a Heat is a transfer of energy (usually thermal energy) from a body of higher temperature to a body of lower temperature. Thermal energy is the energy associated with the random motion of atoms and molecules.	14–15, 18–23
4.2b Temperature is a measurement of the average kinetic energy of the particles in a sample of material. Temperature is not a form of energy.	15, 28–29
4.2c The concepts of kinetic and potential energy can be used to explain physical processes that include: fusion (melting), solidification (freezing), vaporization (boiling, evaporation), condensation, sublimation, and deposition.	16–18, 46–49, 50

THERE IS NO PI 4.3.

Performance Indicator 4.4   Explain the benefits and risks of radioactivity.

Major Understanding	Textbook pp.
4.4a Each radioactive isotope has a specific mode and rate of decay (half–life).	548–549, 552–554
4.4b Nuclear reactions include natural and artificial transmutation, fission, and fusion.	543, 547, 555, 557
4.4c Nuclear reactions can be represented by equations that include symbols which represent atomic nuclei (with mass number and atomic number), subatomic particles (with mass number and charge), and/or emissions such as gamma radiation.	543–546
4.4d Radioactive isotopes have many beneficial uses. Radioactive isotopes are used in medicine and industrial chemistry for radioactive dating, tracing chemical and biological processes, industrial measurement, nuclear power, and detection and treatment of diseases.	553–554, 557–559
4.4e There are inherent risks associated with radioactivity and the use of radioactive isotopes. Risks can include biological exposure, long-term storage and disposal, and nuclear accidents.	542, 557
4.4f There are benefits and risks associated with fission and fusion reactions.	555–557

Key Idea 5:

Energy and matter interact through forces that result in changes in motion.

Performance Indicator 5.2   Explain chemical bonding in terms of the behavior of electrons.

Major Understanding	Textbook pp.
5.2a Chemical bonds are formed when valence electrons are: transferred from one atom to another (ionic); shared between atoms (covalent); or mobile within a metal (metallic).	102, 115–157
5.2b Atoms attain a stable valence electron configuration by bonding with other atoms. Noble gases have stable valence configuration and tend not to bond.	120, 229–231

Major Understanding	Textbook pp.
5.2c When an atom gains one or more electrons, it becomes a negative ion and its radius increases. When an atom loses one or more electrons, it becomes a positive ion and its radius decreases.	99–102, 125–127
5.2d Electron-dot diagrams (Lewis structures) can represent the valence electron arrangement in elements, compounds, and ions.	120–122
5.2e In a multiple covalent bond, more than one pair of electrons are shared between two atoms. Unsaturated organic compounds contain at least one double or triple bond.	121–122
5.2f Some elements exist in two or more forms in the same phase. These forms differ in their molecular or crystal structure, and hence their properties.	128–130
5.2g Two major categories of compounds are ionic and molecular (covalent) compounds.	123–127
5.2h Metals tend to react with nonmetals to form ionic compounds. Nonmetals tend to react with other nonmetals to form molecular (covalent) compounds. Ionic compounds containing polyatomic ions have both ionic and covalent bonding.	127, 128 158, 160
5.2i When a bond is broken, energy is absorbed. When a bond is formed, energy is released.	115
5.2j Electronegativity indicates how strongly an atom of an element attracts electrons in a chemical bond. Electronegativity values are assigned according to arbitrary scales.	102–103
5.2k The electronegativity difference between two bonded atoms is used to assess the degree of polarity in the bond.	121, 126–127
5.2l Molecular polarity can be determined by the shape of the molecule and distribution of charge. Symmetrical (nonpolar) molecules include CO_2, CH_4, and diatomic elements. Asymmetrical (polar) molecules include HCl, NH_3, and H_2O.	130–135
5.2m Intermolecular forces created by the unequal distribution of charge result in varying degrees of attraction between molecules. Hydrogen bonding is an example of a strong intermolecular force.	136–140

Major Understanding	Textbook pp.
5.2n Physical properties of substances can be explained in terms of chemical bonds and intermolecular forces. These properties include conductivity, malleability, solubility, hardness, melting point, and boiling point.	141–143

Performance Indicator 5.3   Compare energy relationships within an atom's nucleus to those outside the nucleus.

Major Understanding	Textbook pp.
5.3a A change in the nucleus of an atom that converts it from one element to another is called transmutation. This can occur naturally or can be induced by the bombardment of the nucleus with high-energy particles.	543–547
5.3b Energy released in a nuclear reaction (fission or fusion) comes from the fractional amount of mass that is converted into energy. Nuclear changes convert matter into energy.	15–16, 554–557
5.3c Energy released during nuclear reactions is much greater than the energy released during chemical reactions.	554–555